Brumbie Dust

Brumbie Dust

A Selection of Stories by
Reginald Ottley

Harcourt, Brace & World, Inc.
New York

First edition

Library of Congress Catalog Card Number: 69-11598

Printed in the United States of America

Contents

Brumbie Dust

Brumbies

Deep in the wild, scarred heart of Australia, wild horses roam the dusty reaches. Just how many there are is difficult to prove, but recent estimates taken by air and land have put the numbers at over a half a million. The horses, or brumbies as they are called, do untold damage to soil and grass as they range over an enormous sweep of country from Cape York in the far north, down to central and southern Australia.

Over the years the herds have been trapped, hunted by riflemen, poisoned with baits and tainted water. Nature's part in the constant war of extermination is the periodic droughts that devastate the country. Yet still the herds survive and multiply in numbers.

As horseflesh, some brumbies are magnificent; long-maned and arrogant-headed, with steely bodies that ripple in the sun. Others are cow-hocked nondescripts, where inbreeding has proved the master.

The size of a herd is governed by the age or virility of its stallion. A young stallion, full-fleshed and power-

ful, may have up to forty mares with their attendant
foals at foot, plus the yearlings and two-year-olds. An
aged or feeble stallion may have only ten or fifteen
mares; perhaps even less. Whatever the number, no
stallion rests secure.

Marauding stallions constantly challenge others for
control of the herds. The fight is to the death. No
quarter is given. And the vicious, ripping battle would
sicken the hearts of most human observers. Stallions
are among the most savage of fighters. Their grunting,
vicious attacks have to be seen to be believed.

Young stallions bred in the herd are allowed to stay
until they show signs of taking interest in the females.
Their sire tolerates no competition. His keen, twitching
ears and bright, savage eyes hear all and see all. With
rib-shattering hoofs, he kicks the youngsters out; drives
them from the herd. When the colts have reached a
bruised and battered acceptance of their fate, the
proud sire trots back to the herd, and the colts are left
to recover and eventually found herds of their own.

All females stay in the herd. A brumbie stallion
serves its own progeny with impartiality. This leads to
a measure of inbreeding, which is counteracted, to
some extent, when the herd is taken over by a new
stallion.

Over the vast sweep of the brumbie country hangs
a constant pall of dust. And in that dust I have ridden
the lonely tracks, seen the blood-red sun rise and set,
and met the lonely people.

If I have re-created a picture of both men and horses in these pages, then I am truly grateful. May the reader enjoy sharing part of my wandering life.

R.O.

The Last of the Horsemen

The rain beat down. Sheer, solid, tumbling blocks of it. You could hear it thud on your hat; feel it slop inside your shirt; swill on your trousers. It was the sort of rain that made you gasp. And when you did, the water running into your mouth choked you. The way things were, it wasn't a good day to be out riding.

But when you have a job to do, and it's fifty miles away, there is no alternative. Leastways, that's how it was with me. I had to push on and cross the Lachlan River at Wheelbar or else be cut off altogether. After six weeks of more or less constant rain, there was more of the river flooding outside its banks than there was inside. Normally fifty yards wide, it had spread to a mile in many places.

As far as a man could see through rain-blurred eyes, water swamped the countryside. Sheets of it. The leaden skies pelted it down. The river choked up and spewed it out across the plains. To me, squelching along on my big bay saddle horse, the world seemed all water. And dangerous water at that. The current's pull eddied around the big bay's legs. I had a pretty good idea what it would be like when we reached the river's banks.

Hunched over on the saddle, I let the bay plod on. He knew, better than I did, what was underfoot. Besides, the rain had soddened me through to the marrow. A niggling ache crawled in my bones. When you get like that, you don't care much what happens; you let the pulpy reins rest loose in your hands and leave it to the horse. If he's no good in the water, your chances don't add up. The big bay was good, so I left him alone.

When he half paddled, half swam around a clump of stump-submerged timber, I wiped the rain from my eyes. Before they could fill again, I made out the country ahead. By the sweep of the river timber, Wheelbar wasn't far. Then my eyes blurred over; the rain smashed my hat brim down.

Ten minutes later, Wheelbar boiled in front of me. I say "boiled" because there's no other word. The bridge was under completely, with only the side rails showing. Swirling, white-capped water tossed feet deep over the bridgeway itself. As far as I could see, water stretched each side of it. The Lachlan had swollen into a sea and was no longer a river.

Be that as it may, what gave me my biggest shock was the sight of a loaded wool wagon. At Wheelbar, roads branch to Carrathool, Hay, and Booligal—of

13

"Hay, Hell and Booligal" fame—a "bush" poem that depicts Hay and Booligal as having similar heat and conditions to the fabled fires of hell. The wagon was on my side of the bridge, near where I judged the Booligal Road to be. Although the wagon stood on what I knew to be fairly high ground, water was up over its five-foot-span wheels; almost, in fact, up to the high platform. The wagon was bogged—bogged hopelessly. Probably down to the hubs in mud.

Four men were wading, hip-deep or more, poking around the wheels. About twenty yards from them, a big cluster of horses stood, rumps turned to the rain. They were packed tightly together. So tight, you could have walked on their backs. Water bubbled and slapped around them. They formed an island of horse-flesh in an angry, restless flood. I guessed there were about seventy of them. Vaguely, beyond them, I saw a further three wagons. But they seemed to be all right. No one was bothering with them. It was the one hull down near the bridge that had all the attention.

Riding toward it, I thought the job of freeing the wagon looked hopeless. Luckily, the four-tiered load of wool bales hadn't tilted. When it did, the whole lot would capsize and be carried away; probably finish up in a treetop somewhere downriver.

I had this in mind as the bay squelched closer. Over his pricked ears, I stared at the teamsters. I don't suppose you can get any wetter than wet; but when you see four men, hip-deep and more in water, with heavy rain beating down on them, wet is not very descriptive. I'll say they had gone beyond saturation and leave it at that.

Two of the teamsters I knew. One was Jimmy Craig, a thick, heavy-set man. The other was "Yacka," a tall, rawboned bushman, famed for his ability with a whip —the four-foot handle, twelve-foot thong variety that outback teamsters use. The other two men I didn't know. They were strangers to me. All four were well on in their fifties.

The way life is in the bush, nobody speaks much when there is trouble. You're expected to use your eyes. If you want to give a hand, you give it. If not, you ride on. Things were rubbing along before you came; they'll rub along after you've gone. That's the general outlook.

And that's the way it was at Wheelbar. I sat on my horse and waited. There's not much sense in having an idle chat with a flood ripping underneath you and rain tipped from a bucket belting down on your head. I had the river to swim, but it could wait. Fourteen tons of wool and a tabletop wagon mean a lot of money. You can't see it float down the river without making some effort. So I waited to give a hand with the effort.

It was Yacka's wagon that was bogged. I knew it by the way the wool load was hitched. He had a method all his own; a kind of treble brace, strained through sheepshank knots. He spent hours once trying to show me, but I never quite got the hang of it.

While I sat and shivered, the four sloshed about, lashing long lengths of rope under the wagon. Over the

roar of rain and flood, I heard snatches about "king
bolt," "Take the strain off 'er," and so on. By some
method or other, they were lashing the under fore-
carriage to the after axle and so taking the strain off
the giant kingpin.

Finally, Jimmy Craig stood up and scratched his
soaked head. Rain bounced off his bald dome while he
did it. Then he and Yacka waded out in front of the
wagon, pushing down with their feet, to test the
ground. The other two men began to flounder toward
the horses. It wasn't hard to guess what was coming,
and I reckoned this would be where I'd be needed.
When I slid from the bay, the water felt warm. I
hitched him to the wagon and plowed after the men.

My guess was right. Yacka had decided to yoke the
four teams to his wagon—all seventy-six horses. They'd
tried two teams before I had arrived, but with no luck.
Now he was going to use the seventy-six horses either
to shift the wagon or "tear 'er in 'alf," as he said.

I don't suppose seventy-six horses have ever been
yoked to a wagon before or since. In dry times, the
normal team is sixteen, strung out in pairs. In the wet
periods eighteen, and sometimes twenty are used, yoked
in the same manner. But seventy-six must be a record.
If they're not, the conditions under which they were
yoked must be—over belly-deep in swirling, muddy
flood waters.

We led them, chains trailing, a pair at a time to the
wagon. Yacka arranged them the way he wanted. A
pair of his own, then several pairs of the other team-

sters' horses. Placing them in that manner, he had horses that knew his voice all along the great team. Wagon teams are driven by voice, not with reins. The teamster stands away from the horses and calls them.

As we built the team, plowing backward and forward, the horses became restless. Those already yoked tried to swing around and huddle in together again. They wanted to swing their rumps to the rain. The others wanted to stay packed tight, for the same reason. We had to squeeze in between them to get to their heads. Some lashed out; others bumped us with their ribs.

No team horse is ever fully broken. He is only taught to lead and have a collar, blinkers, and chains slipped on him. For the rest, he's left pretty much to himself. Never has his feet picked up or any form of gentling. Shoes are an unknown quantity.

When you get horses of that type, under the conditions we had our seventy-six, things are only middling. There's a lot of snorting and kicking going on. And we had trouble keeping our feet. The horses wanted to go one way; we wanted them to go the other. All in all, it wasn't what could be called cozy. But we made it. We finally had the whole seventy-six strung out in pairs.

I took the last half-dozen pairs across, while the rest of the men held the team straight. The last pair were Yacka's leaders—a mare and a gelding who had grown long in the tooth with Yacka. They had obeyed his voice over more miles of track than I'd care to estimate.

The gelding's name was Toby; the mare's, Bonny. The pair of them were massive, in a rawboned way.

When they were yoked, Yacka told them to ease up; stretch the team out a bit. It was good to see. The two leaned into their collars, and gradually, inch by inch, edged forward until the whole of the team's chains were stretched out tight behind them. Every horse was standing straight, settled into his collar.

Then Yacka spat rain from his mouth and waded away to a distance of about twenty yards. The other three teamsters stayed in spaced stages on the near side of the team. I stayed on the off side, to keep an eye on the horses there.

Over the rushing water, above the roar of rain and flood, Yacka's deep voice tightened the horses in their collars.

"Toby," he said. "Bonny. Wedge up there. Wedge up there, or I'll lace your hides."

For a timeless fraction, I thought the horses hadn't heard him. Then his great voice boomed again. Slowly, so slowly you could see him twitch with the strain, Toby heaved in his collar. Bonny did the same. Behind them, one after the other, the rest of the team dipped their heads. The chains at their flanks gleamed in the water. Hoof by sucking hoof, the horses strained forward. How the chains held, I don't know. How the leather rump spiders held, I don't know, either. But I do know the wagon began to roll, surging through the flood, with a crest on its prow.

And Yacka kept the team going. His voice urged

them; coaxed them; swore at them. But you could feel his love for the horses that were straining under his urging.

Then suddenly, the wagon rolled freely. It had reached hard ground, and its weight was nothing for the great team. Pounding through the water, they almost bolted. But Yacka's great voice held them; eased them down slowly. Prick-eared under the calling, Toby and Bonny eased their pulling. The team behind them slacked off, too, without tangling their chains.

On past the other three wagons, the team came to a stop. Yacka waded through the water to take Toby's head. In minutes, we began to unyoke. Still in the driving rain, we yoked them again, each team in its respective wagon.

After I'd unhitched the big bay, I mounted and said so long. The wagons were blurred in the rain sheets when I swam the river.

Over the years, I've thought about Yacka often; thought about the wagon, bogged in the river's flood; thought, too, about the great team straining. I can't help thinking I've seen something that few have seen; seen, too, the last of the great horsemen. Yacka would be gone now, over the earth's horizon.

Stampede

Somewhere in the back country, dust will be rising in a great smother as cattle string past for counting. And somewhere in that smother of dust, a raw-eyed, raw-voiced man, hoarse to the point of strangulation, will croak a final number.

Behind the raw-eyed man, a boss drover will be sitting easy in his saddle. When he nods his head in agreement, another herd of cattle will be ready to roll down the endless miles of dusty, inland stock routes.

Droving is a hard life—possibly one of the hardest lived in this modern world. It will always be hard while ever there are great herds to be traveled over long distances. There are no set hours; no union-governed rules of restrictive practice. The cattle come first, always. There are no halfway measures; "but" this or "but" that. You think cattle, talk cattle, and sleep cattle— that is, when you do sleep, which isn't very often. A drover averages four or five hours' sleep each night, and most of that is uneasy, with one ear eternally open for the sound of restless hoofs. And finally, you eat cattle. You have beef for breakfast, beef for lunch, and beef for the last meal at night. And you love it. If someone offers you mutton or a rasher of bacon, you don't hesitate to tell him what to do with it.

All the men I have traveled cattle with have been of the one type—lean, taciturn, and tough; as tough as they come. Nowhere in the world are they bred tougher. And they're fine fellows. Hard drinking, yes. Hard riding, yes. They don't spare a horse when there's work to be done. Neither do they spare themselves. And in a brawl, they're deadly. Anything goes—spurs, hobble chains, the lot. Yet they're great respecters of women.

You have to have a primitive streak in your nature to endure the life. As the slow miles slip by, day after day, you feel that you're a part of the immensity of earth and sky. You forget what it's like to sleep under a roof or put your feet under a table.

When you go away for a holiday or a break, you feel strange; as if you don't belong. You want to get back and feel the wind in your face, scorching though it may be; or feel the sun on your back. And once you've experienced it, this urge never leaves you. It stays with you until the day you die.

Always, you want to see again the enormous spread of country, where the mirages dance on the horizon and the dust whirls and capers into fantastic whirlie-whirlies. You want to see again the bullocks—great lumbering beasts, washing along before you in a sea of rippling bodies and tossing horns.

At times, the boredom borders on the impossible. You ride slowly for hours on end, with no one to talk to except your horse. Your mates are strung out around the cattle, which often cover two or three square miles, as they graze slowly along. It's surprising what you find to talk to a horse about. Every time he shakes or nods his head to shoo the flies away, you're quite satisfied you've had an intelligent answer.

Other times, when the cattle are touchy, you live in a constant state of tension, frightened sometimes to even rattle a stirrup iron without calling soothingly to the cattle first. The sudden scrape of a match against a box can send a mob of bullocks into the craziest of stampedes.

The season was dry when I joined a mob of nine hundred bullocks traveling down the Barcoo route. There were seven other drovers besides myself, including the boss drover, Bill Shaw.

The cattle were touchy. They came from country where the aborigines still lived in their natural state. The aborigines had strange customs, and one—the one that seemed to affect cattle most—was the use of rancid animal fat, or fat from a dead relative's kidneys, to smear themselves with. When out hunting, sweating under the heat of a fierce sun, they gave off a pretty fearsome smell—something like an abattoir factory that hasn't been properly cleaned. Once cattle had scented the smell, you could never trust them again. However well you handled them on the track, you always knew that the slightest unusual scent or sound would send them galloping into the blue.

We'd had a couple of rushes with them here and there. Half a dozen were killed one night when the mob stampeded and ran into one of those rare occurrences in that part of the world—a fence. The leaders hit the fence first and went down; the remainder bellowed over the top of them. What was left wasn't pleasant to see. The carcasses were trampled flat into the ground. Even the bones were splintered.

Then, toward the end of December—Christmas week, in fact—we began to feel we would end the journey safely. But before we did, we wanted to reach Tipaburra in time for a spree on Christmas Eve.

Tipaburra is only a tiny town consisting of one pub and a dozen houses, but there were some good holding yards where we could put the cattle for the night and push on the next day. As always, the cattle came first, and we weren't worried about Christmas dinner. But we all had a thirst and wanted to make the best of Christmas Eve. We were judging it just right—about twenty miles to go, and the regulation two days to do it in—when we ran into trouble.

We were just easing the bullocks up from their night camp and waiting for the last two night herders to finish their breakfast when a dingo howled suddenly, somewhere out in the half-light. The sobbing, sighing sound brought every bullock scrambling to its feet.

For long moments we all called softly and tried to calm the brutes. But we wasted our time. The dingo howled again, then whimpered chokingly, as if it were being strangled.

That was the final spur. The bullocks bellowed as one and surged away in a great sea of cattle—all nine hundred head of them. And away we went, too. For a long time it was just a matter of flog your horse and hope to stay alive. Then, gradually, sight and sound became adjusted. We sensed, rather than saw, that we were all in a line to drive the cattle around and force them into a great cartwheeling ring.

The sun came up. We were able to see a little better what was happening. But the dust still made it difficult. I know I was riding with a loose rein and screaming insanely, with Joe Murphy about thirty yards ahead of me. He was the only man I could see. The rest were either in front or behind. The countless hoofs, churning up a thick pall of dust, blotted out any further vision.

Gradually, it seemed to me, the cattle were swinging. I looked up in time to see Joe's horse stumble; then a river of bullocks swerved out from the side of the herd, just in front of me and behind Joe. Then they swung in again, and Joe was trapped. He had cattle all around him. How his horse kept his feet in that medley of great horned beasts, I don't know. But there are times when horses seem capable of the impossible.

There was no way out for Joe. A stampede has to take its course. Whoever was ahead of me flogged on. Whoever was behind did the same. I felt sick inside as

I watched Joe fighting with all he knew to keep his horse on its feet. And the horse responded. I could see his flaring nostrils and straining eyes, just above the crackling horns and rolling backs of the great bullocks that dwarfed him. Several times he stumbled, but Joe's iron hand kept him up.

Then I heard Joe swear horribly. A bullock's horn had ripped into his leg, tearing the flesh and smashing a bone. But Joe hung on. He had to. His leg was broken below the knee, and he kept his seat by knee grip and balance.

To me, watching Joe being carried along in that great press of cattle, the time seemed endless. I kept as close to him as I could, but the cattle were like a solid wall of grinding flesh between us.

Slowly, the bullocks began to ease their mad galloping. Those near me were slobbering as they gulped for breath. The madness in their staring eyes changed to a white-balled rolling.

They still stayed packed tight, hemming Joe in. And he was nearly beaten. I could tell that from where I was. He was slumped forward over his horse's withers, but he still had the reins and was helping the horse. I couldn't see his face for the dust. At that time, too, of course, I didn't know his leg was broken; I thought he was just knocked up from the strain.

Eventually, the cattle came around. They swung into a wide, milling circle, and we eased them down to a trot, then a jerky, shuffling walk.

I cut in toward Joe as quickly as I could. At times

like that, it's hard to keep your head. I felt I wanted to shoot every damned bullock in the mob. But it's all part of the job. You have to take it as it comes.

It was a good ten minutes before I could ride in alongside Joe and put my arm around his waist. Then it took another good ten minutes or so before we could work our way to the outside of the herd again. We made it just in time. Joe passed out as soon as we were in the clear.

From there on, we did the best we could, as fast as we could. Bill Shaw left the now steadying cattle and came around to give me a hand to straighten Joe's leg and clean it. He sent another of our team to ride as fast as possible to the nearest homestead, to phone for an ambulance.

We put Joe's saddle under his head for a pillow and made him as comfortable as we could. We were too far away from camp to be able to make him any tea—the bushman's panacea for all ills—but I gave him a drink from my horse's neck waterbag. I remember he went crook on me because I cut his boot off his foot to stop it from swelling. He said they were new, and I'd darn well have to buy him a new pair. I gave him a cigarette instead. He was only kidding about the boots, of course. He was grateful to be alive. I could see it in his eyes.

We left him lying on the ground. It would take an hour or two, maybe more, for an ambulance to arrive. The cattle had to move on. They were still restless and needed a lot of quiet handling.

Bill left a man to keep an eye on Joe. When I looked

back through the dust of the moving herd, the man was fanning Joe with his hat, to keep him cool and shoo away the flies.

Some hours later, the ambulance drove to where we were stringing the cattle along, and we all rode across to say so long to Joe. He was scared—scared of what the starched white nurses would do to him in the hospital.

But when Bill told him that the cook at the hospital was one of the finest in the northwest, Joe's dusty face creased from ear to ear. He lay back, contented.

And that's how we left him—dreaming of his Christmas dinner.

As for the rest of us . . . we rode back to the cattle. We'd lost too much time. We had to bypass Tipaburra and miss out on that Christmas Eve spree.

Bush Secret

The bush holds its secrets; hides them fast in its great, desolate quietness. Where you have ridden, dust covers your tracks. Where you have slept, sand smothers your camp. I've seen whole shanties buried to the rooftops. Yet secrets will out. Call it fate or what you will, men stumble on the hidden—though it's not always found in full—as with me, when it came my turn for finding.

At the time, I rode in a musterer's camp—eight men and a cook, plus a hundred horses. Our job was to muster five hundred square miles of country; all of it raw, scrubby desert land set in the heart of Australia. For the night, we bedded down near a "gilgii," or waterhole. The horses grazed, hobbled, a mile or two away. Grass was scarce near the gilgii, and they had to be held where a sparse growth sprouted. A horse-tailer stayed with them, huddled in his blanket.

Early light found us waiting, bridles looped on arms, for the horses to be driven in.

They arrived as the cook shouted, "She's on, boys.
Come and eat it, or I'll toss it in the fire."

Gravel-voiced though he was, his heart was right.
He'd hold our tucker forever if there was work to be
done. So we saddled before hunkering down around
the fire. The steak tasted good, washed down with hot
black tea.

After the meal, orders were simple. Stockwork in the
big country is more by instinct than command. Cattle
follow a pattern of sectional grazing. Whole areas won't
show a hoof mark; then you find a patch where the
hoof pads are deep; there's a fair-sized herd in the district. A man has to go on his own flair and judgment—
also his sense of direction. Many a "new chum" has
found cattle and driven them away from where the
main herd is gathering.

However, be that as it may, Ross, the overseer, called
after me when we were leaving.

"Take that gully to the west, Reg. She stretches for
twenty miles, then on into 'bad country.' There's a bull
there ya' c'n put a bullet in. He's a 'scrubber' I saw last
year."

Ross was a man who never argued, and a man who
never forgot. Twenty-thousand head ranged on Yomba,
and he knew every one—or close to it, anyway.

When I reached the gully, the sun lipped behind me.
Hazy scarlet flamed on the skyline as I rode the gully's
rim. My thought was to scour the mile or so wide side
of the gully I was on and drive any cattle I found down
to the center. On the return journey, I'd scour the other

side, while bunching the earlier gathered cattle ahead of me.

It's a job almost as difficult to do as it is to explain. The difference is the amount of hard riding. My horse was lathered before he covered eight or nine miles. Then, in the manner of outback horses, the sweat hardened; caked on his flanks. For the rest of the day he'd be bone dry, except under the saddle. Nature has a way of solving problems. Inuring a beast to heat is one of them.

Riding steadily, and always searching, I came toward the end—near where Ross had said the gully ran into bad country. I suppose, by then, I'd turned down two hundred cattle; maybe more, maybe less; it's difficult to say when the mobs are stringing past. You see a bunch gallop along one pad; then another mob breaks somewhere else. So long as they're heading the right way, you don't bother too much. A rough count gives you some idea of how many you should have in the final bunching.

Before swinging across to start the ride back, I had a final scan around. It was noon by then, and the sun poured down. You could feel it bite through shirt and trousers. Hat over eyes, I peered up a sandstone outcropping. Halfway up its face, in a scatter of jumbled rocks, twenty odd cows sprawled in shaded comfort. A big rock edge leaned over them. With the hot wind that was blowing, it must've been a cool spot.

But cool spot or not, they had to come down. Eager-footed, my horse clawed his way on the long climb up.

He had to climb out of sight of the cattle, or they would have broken and gone helter-skelter before we could turn them.

Always I had the thought of the bad country beyond. Chasing a galloping mob through it would be no picnic; and there's always the problem of tracking out before sunset.

Luckily, we kept hidden. Still slipping and scraping, we circled around the far side of the cattle, then worked our way in toward them.

I'd just uncoiled my whip when I saw the bull. High above me, he stood on the peak of a bluff. A sheer drop fell away beneath him. At three hundred yards or more, he was too far away for a sure shot. Bulls are tough. You need to be close to kill them humanely.

Without description, I knew he was the scrubber Ross wanted shot. This fellow was red, with great curved horns on his head. His bellow, when it came, echoed high, thin, and piercing; the true bawl of a wild bush scrubber.

My horse heard the call, and I had to nudge him to edge along after the cows; he wanted to wheel upward after the outlaw bull. A good horse is like that, if he's trained to the working of cattle.

With the cows driven down, I let him have his head for the long, scraping climb upward. The bull waited until we were two-thirds up, then broke away, suddenly. I saw the angry whisk of his tail and the dusty stamp of his hoofs; then he was gone. All that was left was a drifting dust swirl.

Still climbing, we reached the crag. Droppings and tracks showed the bull had camped there a long time. You could see the hollows where he'd stretched full length. But of the bull himself, neither horn nor hoof showed.

I went to rein away and search for fresh tracks when the horse nickered. His prick-eared head nuzzled downhill, toward the bad country. In the shadow of a rock, I saw a darker blur of shade. The bull was there, using bush camouflage.

I freed my thirty-two—it's a light rifle and easy to carry. Over scarred, eroded sandstone we skidded down, in the hope of drawing close. A rattle of stones, kicked forward by my horse, ended the hope. The bull snorted once, then bolted. High-tailed, he raced nimble-footed as any mountain deer. Flat to the withers, I spurred after him.

Well, I've had some rides. Some of them, even now, have me hanging onto the bedrail. But that one still makes me sweat. Over crumbling rock; down sudden drops; up slippery slopes. All at a wild, crazy gallop. My horse had his head to go where he liked. I threw him the reins and hoped for the best. Up ahead of us, the bull leaped and snorted. Scrubbers are more greyhound than bull. Big-chested, lean-gutted, they do great damage to breeding herds and have to be destroyed. They'll rip a good beast to pieces.

This one dived down a long, slippery slope. Skating on hocks and rump, my horse slid after him. You could smell the tail hairs burning. At the bottom, the bull tumbled, *holas bolas.* Horn over tip, he plowed a furrow that nearly brought us down.

As luck would have it, my horse was ready. He hurdled the bull's belly, then wheeled to give me a chance. I shot the bull, neatly and cleanly. No kick. No struggle. He never knew what hit him. In fact, he sighed, as if glad it was over. Wild cattle lead an outlaw life that gives them little contentment.

With half my day's work over, the problem was to find my way back. The sun had angled, and my horse had tired; he needed some slow walking to recover. Keen while the hunt was on, he had galloped for hours from excitement. But, as in men, the reaction set in. He plodded tiredly, while I tried to backtrack. But some slopes you ride down, you can't ride up. There just isn't any footing, and a detour throws you out; eroded rock looks much the same from any angle.

Finally, I rode across a bare, burnished strip of claypan—eroded soil scoured to the hard, baked subsoil. On the far side stretched a straggle of withered needlewoods.

I thought they might lead to a breakthrough; a chance to reach the gully. They did, in a way. But, more important, they led to something else. I'd reached the last tree when I saw it.

Tethered to a spiky limb hung a dead horse—or I should say, the skeleton of a horse. The bridle reins were sun-shrunk to long, thin strings, but still strong enough to hold up the bony head. On the skeleton's vertebrae lay the remnants of a saddle. Sun-shrunk, too, it was half its original size. The leather had pulled from the saddle tree. Years must have passed—maybe twenty or thirty—since the horse had died. The mystery was, among others, how the bones had lasted. Sun must have cured instead of powdering.

There was so much sadness in the sight that I turned away. You could hear the rustle of hoofs haunting the great bush quietness. And as I rode, I wondered what had happened. Who had tethered the horse to a light, spiky bough?

A properly broken horse can be tied with cotton; it will stay tied until it dies. This one had done so. Who had done the tying? And where was he now? There's only one answer in the hot, dry country. A man on his feet, lost, without water, is dead before two suns have set. You could ride forever and never find his bones.

I was tired when I drove my cattle on to camp. A large herd had grown during the long, hot day. Ross, the overseer, stood waiting near the herders.

"How d' yer go?" he asked. "Did yer shoot the bull or find any traces?"

"Yeah," I said, "he's dead," and turned away.

The bush holds its secrets. Why talk if you don't know the full answers?

Dusty Deal

I didn't see Momba when he rode around the river's bend just above my camp. I had other things to worry me. A few seconds before, I'd kicked a hollow log into the fire, thinking it would make a good backstop. But that's as far as my thoughts went. An angry snake hissed out of the log and went over my boot. I kicked him off. He slid under my blankets. From there on, we sparred, blindfold. The snake couldn't see me; I couldn't see the snake. It was all right, as far as those sorts of situations go, but sooner or later I had to sleep—and a man can't sleep with a snake.

As the minutes passed, I stared at every fold in the blankets. Not a movement. I poked with a stick. Not a crease stirred. Not a slither whispered. I'd just decided to flick up a blanket and take a chance on wrapping the snake around my neck when Momba reined in behind me. I heard his horses, but didn't turn around. You don't when there's a snake in front of you—they move too fast. One flicker and they're gone—either into the distance or up your trouser's leg.

Anyway, Momba guessed why I was hind up in the dust. He creaked down out of the saddle to heel-scuff over to me. Close to my rump, he stared down without speaking. For the time it takes to tell, we both stared; Momba standing up, me squatting down.

Some men have a way with snakes that leaves you cold; sends the shivers crawling down your back. Momba did. His hawk eyes saw a wrinkle in the blankets I couldn't see. Without bothering to take what seemed to me normal precautions, he slid a hand in under the wool. When he jerked upright, I thought he'd been bitten. But he hadn't. Instead, he had the snake's tail gripped in his hand.

While I ducked, he whirled the flash of long, silver belly around his head, then cracked it—just as a man would a whip. The snake's head almost exploded from its body. For a wriggle or two, Momba held the still squirming body in his hand, then dropped it in the fire.

From the way he spat, you could tell Momba considered the matter ended, although he did go on to say, while he scrubbed his hand down his trousers, "Snakes ain't nothin'. Not if you treat 'em right."

Maybe they're not. It all depends on what he meant by "right." But I had to admit, his way was as good as any.

By the time I'd finished telling him how I'd come to tangle with the snake in the first place, the sun had almost set. With his eyes on my well-stuffed saddlebags, Momba said he reckoned he'd camp with me for the night. One of his horses was lame; he didn't want to travel any further. Not for that day, at any rate.

When he mentioned his horses, I noticed for the first time he had four; one he rode, one he packed, and two "running spare." It was one of these that was lame. It had a big split down the center of its hoof—a fairly common complaint in the back country and one almost impossible to heal or cure completely. Once a horse has it, you can nearly always write it off as a dead loss.

Glad to have some company, I boiled the billy while Momba unsaddled. Then we hunkered down each side of the fire. The tea had a burned snake flavor, but otherwise was good. So was the damper, with a slice of corned beef between. When you've been in the saddle all day, you don't judge a meal by its flavor; you judge it by its quantity. If it pushes out the wrinkles, it's good enough.

With the last flavored mouthful still in his mouth, Momba stood up. He must have been at least eighty, yet he moved with ease. His lean old body had a desert stringiness; tough and unyielding. He said he reckoned he'd take a walk down by the river; find the mate of the snake he'd killed. Otherwise, we'd be up all night chasing the ruddy thing.

I was with him all the way. It's an accepted fact that snakes travel in pairs. If you kill one, the other will come looking for it. Yet when I offered to go with him, Momba shook his head.

"No," he said. "A man knows where he's putting his own feet, but he don't know where somebody else is puttin' his'n." And away he went.

For the next quarter of an hour, I sat in silence. It was getting dark, and the shadows danced around the fire. Then some of the finest swearing I've ever heard ripped into the sunset. Momba came up over the riverbank carrying another snake. It was the same breed as the other one and about the same size. Within moments it followed its mate into the fire.

Having solved the snake problem, we turned in—although I must admit I had thoughts that maybe the pair had relatives. But Momba's snore soon convinced me. Rolled over in my blankets, I followed him into "spirit-land."

In the morning, Momba scraped his lean old face and worried about his horse; asked me if I'd give him a hand to shoe it. Said he knew a trick or two to fix the split if I'd hold the hoof up for him. Being the kind who likes to fool around with horses, I said I would. So we left it at that, while Momba finished his shave.

After breakfast he brought the horse into camp. I don't think it had ever had its feet picked up. But it had to learn sometime. While I battled to keep the hoof off the ground, Momba gouged soft resin out of a nearby gum tree. With it, he filled in the crack, smoothing it around with his finger. Then he rubbed dust on the resin surface while it was still soft. When he'd finished, you couldn't see where the crack had been. To complete the deception, he trimmed both front hoofs to a likeness and tacked on two old shoes. He would have fooled a college full of vets.

By the time Momba had driven the last nail, I was through. I'd wrestled over a good two acres of country, but it was worth it for the horse's sake. Even if only temporarily, he could at least walk freely. As for Momba, the wink that split his weathered old face would've done credit to a cattle duffer.

"He'll be right," he said. "He'll hold together for a week or two, an' by that time I'll be out of him."

All's fair in love and horse dealing, and the camouflage is much the same. We had a billy of tea on the strength of it, then saddled our horses. I had two; Momba had his four. With the sun on our left cheeks, we headed down the river.

In the few hours I'd known him, I'd gathered Momba was a saddle tramp. He followed the grass and water. At the time, there had been good rains to the south. He was headed that way. I was also saddle loose, but intended to swing west at Wilcannia Bridge; so we agreed to travel that far together, then separate.

In the way of men whose life is spent with horses, we jogged quietly along. No fuss. No hurry. Where the grass was good, we camped. Where it was spare, we pushed on.

Toward the end of the third day, Wilcannia Bridge showed in the distance. Even on the river, heat haze distorted vision. But Momba had incredible eyesight. He pulled his hat low and, after a minute or two, spat over the pommel.

"If that ain't ole Jud's buggy camped over by the bridge," he said, "I'll ride a flea into Bourke an' spur 'im all the way."

I didn't know who old Jud was, but Momba soon told me. From the description, I gathered Jud was so low, he could crawl under a snake's belly—and he would have so much room, he could put up an umbrella. Further, he'd crawl into any position to twist a man.

Yet when we reined in near the buggy, Momba expressed surprise. His gaunt face creased in pleasure. If I hadn't been listening to him for the last few minutes, I'd have believed every word he cracked down at Jud. And Jud was the same. Told us to make ourselves at home; spread our blankets where we liked.

This was all right by me, but didn't seem to suit Momba. Before he climbed out of the saddle, I noticed he had a quick glance at Jud's horses, tied on a picket line. There were six, all feeding from boxes. Unlike Momba and me, Jud could, and did, carry chaff in his buggy.

After I'd hobbled my horses, I came back, expecting to see Momba do the same. Instead, he hitched his four to a nearby tree. With the setting sun red on his face, he said he'd push on later, "Git in a bit of travelin' while the moon's cool."

I didn't argue. Neither did Jud. A man's free to come and go as he likes. There are no set rules in the bush. But I couldn't help wondering. It wasn't like Momba to pass up the chance of a good night's camp.

When all the chores were finished, we settled down for a meal. In a flare of dancing flames, Jud passed around chops, pumpkin, and damper. He loaded our plates. Where he'd got it all from, I don't know. There are times when you don't ask questions—you just eat. This was one of them. When the plates were all scraped, we sat back and yarned, mostly about horses.

Finally, Momba shaded his eyes from the fire and said, "I see yer still got the old bay mare."

Jud didn't answer for a minute. He was busy poking at the fire. When he straightened, he held a glowing stick to his pipe. You could see his coppery skin shining through the smoke.

"Yeah," he said. "I still got 'er. She's as fat as mud."

After he'd said it, he dropped the stick back in the fire, and for a while no one spoke. Then Jud long-legged it over to the buggy. When he came back, he had a bottle of wine in his hand.

"We'll 'ave a swoller," he said, "t' lay the dust. A man gits dry, talkin'."

A man gets dry all right. While Jud poured, I passed up the pannikins. Then we hunkered down again, with the pannikins in our hands.

With the wine warm on his tongue, Jud went on to tell us all about the mare. What a rattling bit of horse-flesh she was. He had never known her to put a foot wrong. She could turn on a sixpence. Got the best pair of hocks this side of the border.

When Jud had run dry, Momba came in for the chorus. "Yer know, Jud," he said, "I've allus liked that

41

mare. Had me mind on her for a long time. Ever since I last saw ya'."

"'Ave yer now?" Jud almost whispered when he said it. You could see the cords jerking in his neck.

He took out his pipe to spit, then hiked it over to the buggy. Back in the fire glow, another bottle glittered over our mugs.

"Yeah," Momba went on. "I wouldn't mind ownin' 'er. Jest suit me t' breed a foal from."

After he'd said that, the chips were in the fire. You could smell them frying. Tipping his gaunt old head to let the wine flow down, he told us all about his horse—the bay we had shod. What a great horse he was. Sound as a bell. Not a blemish on him. The only trouble was, he was a gelding.

"An' it don't matter how hard yer try, you got a grasshopper's chance in a sandstorm of gittin' a foal from a gelding."

Jud nodded at this bit of reasoning. He never bothered with foals himself, but he could see Momba's point. The bottle gleamed again as he poured from it. With a full pannikin held just under his chin, he stared across at Momba.

"Ya're right," he said. "Dead right. What was yer figurin' on doin' with 'im?"

Momba shifted his rump. His spurs were jutting into him. A man gets cramped when he squats too long.

"Trade 'im," he said. "Swap 'im for the right kind of mare."

The way Jud looked, you would have thought he was surprised.

"Was yer now?" he said. "Now ain't that unusual?" He stared into the fire, sipping his wine. You had to hand it to him. He was good. Not a line quivered on his wrinkled old face. With great emphasis, he went on to tell Momba he'd do him a favor. He'd swap his mare for Momba's gelding. But—and here he scruffed a finger down his nose—not because he wanted t' get rid of the mare, but because he an' Momba were mates. They'd known each other, on an' off, since they were knee high to a pup.

The upshot was, they wandered off into the darkness to look at their respective horses. Momba carried a lantern; Jud swayed by his side. In the time they were gone, I unrolled my blankets, getting set for the night.

When they came back, the deal was clinched. And to celebrate, Jud opened another bottle. This sealed the deal. By bush law, it was unbreakable.

After the pannikins were emptied, Momba rocked to his feet. He reckoned he'd be on his way. Get a bit of dust under him. Jud shook his hand. So did I. There wasn't much else I could do. As I have said, all is fair in love and horse dealing.

Not an eyelid flickered when Momba said so long, he'd be seeing me. And I reckoned he would. Then he was gone. His tall old figure faded into the darkness.

For a few minutes, Jud and I listened to the hoof-beats. Finally, they rattled over the bridge to merge into the night quietness. Not a sound broke the stillness around the camp. The fire flickered in loneliness. I went back to it. Jud reached for another bottle inside the buggy.

"Yer know," he said, as he poured into our panni-kins, "it's not often a man does a deal like that. Not of-ten at all."

I held my pannikin steady and stared into the fire. The logs had crumbled into heaps of glowing coals. "I've allus wanted t' have a crack at ole Momba. He did me once over a deal."

There are times when a man feels he's choking. He has to get away. I stood up to go to my blankets.

"Yeah," Jud said. "Now I've done it. Tossed 'im right into the bullpen. That ole mare I've swapped 'im 'as a crack in 'er hoof as big as yer hand. I spent a whole day last week filling it. Filled it with resin. Gave it a nice finish. Dust an' all. Even ole hawkeye Momba couldn't spot it. What d' yer think of that?"

I didn't tell him. I couldn't. I crawled over to my blankets and pulled them up over my head. It was hot, but I had to stay there. I was as close to choking as I've ever been.

Brumbie Running

Camped close to a lonely gilgii, Mick and I squatted, rump on bootheels, hunkered down in the dust. With sticks in our hands, we drew dust maps of different districts we knew where brumbies were known to be. I can see now Mick's lean, tough face as we argued. He wanted to go to one place; I wanted to go to another.

Finally, we dug in our pockets for that solver of all bush arguments—a penny. I found one and tossed it; Mick groveled around in the dust, watching where it rolled. He called heads; I called tails.

The penny bowled down toward the gilgii, then tipped over, upfaced to the sun. Even from where I stood, I didn't need to hear Mick's calloused fingers click to know that he had won. I could see the king's head under its coating of dust.

After Mick had flipped the penny back to me, he set the billy on the fire. Over more mugs of tea than I can remember, I watched his stick scraping diagrams on the ground; dried watercourses, gullies, stretches of lignum-studded claypans, which Mick said stretched for miles. It was against these sun-dried lignum swamps that I had argued in the first place, before tossing the penny.

Lignum is treacherous from the angle of finding a way through its mazelike tangle. The spear-leafed bush grows to a height of about eight feet and is a monotonous gray in color. Growing in close-rooted clumps over an area covering several square miles, the whole presents a forbidding aspect; something similar, in appearance, to a great sweep of blue-gray water glistening grayly in the sun. From experience, I knew what it was like inside these far-spread lignum stands. You have to remember every angle of the sun to find your way about, and if it's nighttime, you have to keep one eye turned up to the stars. Unlike other trees or shrubs, lignum doesn't seem to weather on the prevailing wind's side—a characteristic that makes it more confusing.

However, the dry lignum claypans give great cover to the wild brumbie herds. The shrub is edible, though tough and stringy when chewed. Both horses and cattle can graze on it for a long period without harmful effects—an invaluable asset when drought is scouring every grass blade from the earth's surface or hunters are perched with high-powered rifles, overlooking the grasslands.

The area Mick mapped in the dust stretched from the arid salt lakes beyond Yancannia, toward the South Australian border. It was harsh, desolate country at the best of times, but typical brumbie country, covering stark, broken foothills, as well as flat claypan barrenness.

Once out there, we were entirely on our own. If we had a fall with a horse or were dragged in the stirrup, we would have to do the best we could—set a broken bone with the round green bark cut from a sapling or lie under a tree for days, while the other rode for help.

That was one of the things we discussed while Mick sketched with his stick. We decided to buy another couple of horse bandages and a tin of Condy's crystals —a fine disinfectant and a big help in the case of snake bite, if you suck the wound first.

At one point in his diagram, Mick prodded with his stick. He remembered, he said, seeing an old set of stockyards somewhere about there. It was years ago, and he'd been over a lot of ground since then, but he thought he could find them, once he got close and the lay of the country came back to him. I stared at the hole he was digging with the stick and said I hoped he could. It would save us a great deal of hard manual work—something most horsemen are averse to, particularly when it has to be done under a broiling sun.

The fact of the yards being there was not unusual. In the 1880's and early 1900's, pioneers trekked over the great outback. Some built stockyards to handle their cattle in; others built bush shacks, the remains of which can also still be seen. Back country timber has an indestructible quality.

What happened to those early pioneers is known only to the dust that drifts over the land covering their bones. Many were speared by aborigines. Many died of thirst or hearts broken by the constant fight against adversity. The vast, lonely cattle empires scattered there today stand monument to those who were lucky or perhaps more fitted to the task.

By the time Mick finished scratching his map, the sun had almost set. Great streaks of blood-red haze crawled low on the western sky.

While Mick rocked bow-leggedly down to the gilgii for another billyful of water, I tipped a tin of sausages into a frying pan. They were spluttering happily when he came back and set the billy on the opposite side of the fire.

Over a meal of sausages tucked in between hunks of damper, we continued our planning. As I reckoned up the amounts of different tinned stores we would need, Mick scratched them in the dust; the same with flour, tea, and sugar.

When we'd finished eating, I copied the list onto the sweat flap of my saddle. I used a shoeing nail for a pencil. I've always been partial to a saddle-sweat flap for a writing pad. It's something you don't mislay or lose.

The next day, we rode across country to Whitecliffs, a small town consisting of pub, store, police station, and a dozen or so houses built on an old opal mining site.

Outside the sun-cracked boarding of the general store, we halted our cavalcade of horses. We had ten altogether; two we were riding, three with packs on their backs, and five running loose. Close to the store's wooden veranda, they clustered in trained formation, tail-switching the flies from their rumps. The heat was fantastic. Glare from the white rocks encircling the town made us screw our eyelids.

After we had said good day to the storekeeper, Mick held the door open while I stood by my saddle horse and bellowed out our order. In a land where sun-dehydrated men do strange things, the storekeeper must have thought it an unusual way to take an order. But he showed no surprise. His big leathery hands snatched down tins from the shelves as fast as I could read from my saddle.

When I slapped my horse on the rump and walked around past his heels into the store, our big order towered on the counter, plus three or four sacks the storekeeper dumped on the floor. Two coils of wire were added to these, along with a heap of three dozen empty sacks.

Mick and I dug deep into our wallets to pay for the goods, then started to stow them in the pack bags. The storekeeper gave us a hand. With the money we had paid him stuffed in his hip pocket, he trudged backward and forward with the tins and sacks.

When the last sack had been strained down under a surcingle, we all went next door to the pub. The storekeeper wouldn't let us pay for any drinks. He said he reckoned the shout was on him. I reckon it was, too.

By the time Mick and I climbed back into the saddle, we had, in theory, yarded every brumbie from Cape

York Peninsula to the South Australian desert. I did, in fact, during the afternoon in the bar, bet an Afghan camel teamster that I could ride his bull camel. When he brought the grunting, slobbery-jawed brute around behind the pub, the animal looked as big as a house. It bellowed and spat frothy spittle over the Afghan before he could get it to lie down for the saddle to be strapped behind its hump. To say I rode the brute would be an understatement, but when it roared its last ear-shattering bellow, I was still in the saddle. The old Afghan couldn't believe his eyes.

After we left Whitecliffs, Mick and I rode westward, following the cattle overlanders' route. For two or three days, we had the vast spread of dusty emptiness all to ourselves and our hoof-shuffling cavalcade of horses. Then a great flood of cattle, ringed around with silent riders, flowed over the horizon.

While we watched, the herd seemed to flow endlessly, smothered under a rolling cloud of dust. When they drew close, we saw they were bullocks; big-horned fellows, with Northern Territory brands scarred on their hides. There were well over two thousand of them.

That night we camped with the drovers, about half a mile away from their cattle. We were lucky. It was the drovers' night to kill a beast for fresh meat—something Mick and I hadn't tasted for several weeks.

While three men eased their horses into the herd to select a prime beast, the boss drover cocked his rifle and waited near a stunted tree. When the three men, in a flurry of fast-pounding horseflesh, drove the bullock toward him, the boss slowly raised his rifle. He stood squarely in front of the beast until the great horns were almost close enough to rip; then he squeezed the trigger. The bullock tumbled at his feet, directly under the tree. I've done the same thing myself since, but it's a nervy way to kill a beast, particularly to those who are watching.

In a matter of minutes, the men had the bullock bled, skinned, dressed, and hanging up in the tree—no water to wash down afterwards, or anything like that. Drovers can't carry the niceties of abattoirs with them, but it's surprising how clean, neat, and efficient they can be.

'Later in the night, to the sound of the distant rider's mournful singing and the restless lowing of cattle, Mick and I helped the cook dry-salt most of the carcass. It was the only way we could repay the boss drover for the great hunk of steak he gave us.

At daylight, after a yarn-filled, tea-drinking night, the lean-faced horse-tailer brought our horses on to camp, along with his own. The air vibrated with the stamp of hoofs and the whinnying bustle.

Packed and saddled, Mick and I said so long to the cattle drovers. They said so long to us; hoped to see us around sometime. The last we saw of them they were tiny specks, dotted around their cattle. To our glare-slitted eyes, the massive herd seemed infinitely small in the vast amphitheater of sun and dust. The great outback can dwarf the mightiest of things.

For several days our horses jog-shuffled slowly, covering thirty to thirty-five miles a day. The hours were long—long to a point where the boredom became habitual. We rode with our shoulders hunched over, hats pulled low over our eyes, and our weight balanced in the sun-hot stirrup irons. Heat poured down on us with pitiless intensity. We had to travel slowly to save our horses for the hard riding that lay ahead of them.

At times, when the heat-crazed mirages danced on the horizon, Mick and I used to clear our dusty throats and talk about the pubs in Sydney—long marble bars, with ice-cold beer gushing out of the taps—or being on a beach, pounded by the great Pacific breakers. But when we unsaddled for the midday break or the night camp, we ceased to think about ice-cold beer. Hot tea, drunk near a fire of sun-dried cattle chips, was better. We drank it black, scalding hot, and with very little sugar. Billyful after billyful washed down our dust-coated gullets, and we loved every billyful. Each one was better than the last.

Nearing Yancannia, we left the stock route and struck across country. According to Mick's reckonings when we were camped at the gilgii, we could save about fifty miles by doing so. Fifty miles is fifty miles when you have ten sweat-caked horses to consider. They were holding their condition well, and we wanted to keep them that way. Apart from the distance-saving factor, we always had to think about grass, feed, and water. The great herds passing through Yancannia did not leave too much of either.

Close to the final stages of our journey, we met a gaunt, weathered giant of a man. He was sprawled under a bush, with his head resting on a camel saddle, when we rode into a gully to camp for the night. His two hobbled camels grazed on a clump of scrub close to the gully's rim. A small fire of sticks smoldered near the man's big feet; a blackened billy rested close to his hand. He looked a picture of lonely, sun-blackened contentment as he puffed at a hook-stemmed pipe.

The contentment didn't last. With a soul-shattering curse that condemned Mick and me to every form of roasting in hell, the big man catapulted up from the ground. On bare, calloused feet, he pranced around, shaking his ham-sized fists and asking what the so-and-so we meant by breaking in on his privacy. Wasn't the bush big enough for us to find somewhere else to camp?

Mick and I sat easy in our saddles and scratched our heads. It wasn't difficult to see that the man was a "hatter"—one of the occasional men you meet in the great outback who have been driven mad by heat, loneliness, or a combination of the whole. They are, as a rule, harmless and keep snakes or bush rats for pets, or else a cockatoo, to all of which they talk nonsense for hours on end.

Others are unreliable; violent in their reaction toward anyone who trespasses on the loneliness that obsesses them. Left alone, they usually simmer down or else pack up and leave the disputed camping site to the new arrival.

We decided to see what course the big man prancing on the other side of the gully would take. We were not sure how far ahead the next waterhole was. In any case, we couldn't have found it before darkness set in.

We unpacked slowly, keeping one eye on the gaunt, shaggy-bearded man, the other on the job in hand. When we led our horses down toward the scummy sun-cracked mud in the center of which stretched a narrow strip of water, we ran into trouble.

The horses scented where the camels had churned the mud with their big pads. It took us a good sweating, cursing hour before we could get our horses to drink. The gaunt-faced man, now squatting by his fire, scowled his disapproval. He made no attempt to pack.

When our fire crackled into a blaze, Mick and I hunkered down near it to cook a meal. With the setting sun hot in our faces, we pretended not to notice the big man opposite. It was a difficult thing to do. He had boiled another billyful of tea and was arguing with himself. Waving his hands about as he gulped great mouthfuls of tea, he looked a strange, demented sight.

I told Mick that I thought we ought to roll up in our blankets close together. If the big hatter got crawling around in the night, he might take a lot of handling, and we would have to do it without hurting him or getting hurt ourselves. The nearest human habitation was probably seventy to eighty miles away.

Mick nodded in agreement. He liked a brawl with the next man, but a tousle with the big, rock-hard man whose brain was obviously turned would be more than a brawl. It might be sheer, downright massacre. I suppose what we should have done was pack our gear again and push on—camp somewhere out in the scrub and leave the hatter to his waterhole.

Anyway, being tired, we turned in. Several hundred yards away, our horses rattled their neck bells, feeding on the sparse grass. On the far side of the gully, we could hear the camels grunting as they regurgitated their cuds.

Everything was normal, except for the dim glow of the fire over which the big man crouched. The dull red glow tinged his face and beard to a fierce copper color. His muttering voice sounded guttural, muffled in the gully's banks.

It must have been well after midnight when I awoke. I have always been a light sleeper, able to wake at the slightest sound or when I set my mind. This time, I knew it was something different. The soft waves of horror crawling on the back of my neck told me that.

For a second's fraction, I didn't think of the hatter; my brain wasn't fully adjusted. I first glanced sideways at Mick, rolled tight in his blankets close to my side. He was sound asleep and breathing deeply, with a blanket's corner drawn over his face.

Then I heard a short, whispering sigh. It was the hatter; he was almost on top of me. The smell of his stale tobacco-rank breath puffed in my face.

From there on, the night erupted with violence. The hatter clamped his full weight on top of me, trying to pin my arms. One of his steely legs kicked Mick, waking him suddenly.

While I fought to keep the hatter's hands away from my face, Mick cursed every blanket that was ever milled. He couldn't throw his off quickly enough.

When he did struggle free, I had a grip on the hatter's wrists, trying to twist them. But I lost the grip. Mick smashed down on the hatter and drove his hairy face into mine. I felt the blood splatter from my nose; then the combined weight of the two men on top of me drove every pound of wind from my lungs.

Mick got a headlock on the hatter and wrenched him over backward. This time Mick was underneath when I, in turn, groped for a grip on the big man's neck. Finally, I grabbed him by his beard with one hand and the hair on top of his head with the other. Then I screwed with every sinew I had—screwed until I thought his neck would crack.

Mick helped matters along by twisting out from under and straddling the hatter's broad back. Between us we held him, face jammed down in the dust. Neither Mick nor myself were small men. Years of handling rough horses had toughened us to a point of bone and muscle hardness. Yet we barely held him. Several times I felt that if he gave one more heave, we would lose our grips.

The long, sobbing minutes passed. Each of us strained every tight, rigid muscle. Then suddenly, the hatter relaxed. Choked with the blood from my fast swelling nose, I felt the big body sink. Mick did, too.

And strange as it may seem, we felt the madness flow out of the hatter. It was a strange feeling, but true. Over many campfires afterwards, Mick and I argued about the unusual incident. We were both sure of one thing. We definitely felt the madness leave the hatter.

Gradually, I eased my hands from the mass of tangled hair and beard. Mick sat quietly on the small of the man's back before he slid sideways, crouching in the dust. We waited, holding our breaths but feeling fairly confident. I wiped some of the blood from my mouth.

For a few moments the hatter stayed where he was, face down and spread-eagled full length. Then he rolled over to sit up. It was too dark to see him clearly, yet we could sense the change. For the time being at any rate, he was a normal man. Half dazed, he scrambled to his feet, while Mick and I watched. None of us spoke.

Still without speaking, the hatter padded on his bare feet down the gully. The last we ever saw of him was his shadowy figure moving through the darkness. Later, we heard the complaining grunts of his camels as he packed and saddled them. The gray light of dawn was barely showing when we heard the soft swish of camel pads whispering out of the gully.

A day or two later, Mick reined in his horse when we crested the brow of a spur. I jogged up beside him, and we shaded our eyes to stare around at the surrounding country.

The enormous sweep of stark, rugged grandeur did not interest us. It was little different from elsewhere in the great outback. What did interest us was the amount of horse droppings we had seen and the numbers of hoof tracks.

We were in brumbie territory. The lignum claypans Mick had mentioned while we were camped on the gilgii stretched in waves before us.

Finally, Mick pointed to a clump of scrub timber close to the edges of the lignum. On the other side of the timber, he reckoned we would find the old stockyards—that's if his memory served him right. After jogging our cavalcade over a couple of miles of rough going, we reached the timber. Threading our way through it, we found the old stockyards, still upright and in good shape.

Feeling that so far was so good, we stretched our legs by walking around the big posts, getting an idea of how much work we would have to do before the yards would be usable. Surprisingly, it was little enough. Despite their age, most of the posts and rails were in excellent condition. Weathered by sun and wind to a bleached hardness, they would stand for another fifty years.

From our hat-tipped, saddle-stiff inspection of the stockyards, we turned to that most important of all questions—water. According to Mick's rapidly reviving memory of the district, there were two watering points within a workable radius—obviously the reason for the yards being built there in the first place. No one would build them unless he knew permanent water was nearby. In the dry country you only find stock within walking distance of water. Near the water is the logical place to put a set of yards.

My own thoughts, while we were walking around the yards, were that they had been built by someone after the same stock as ourselves, namely brumbies; perhaps as long ago as the early 1900's, when remounts for India were bringing a good price. The yards seemed to me to be designed more for the handling of horses than they were for cattle.

Mick said that one waterhole lay to the westward, about a mile away. It was a natural seepage or soak, more or less permanent. The yards faced westward, so that was a good watering spot to leave alone as the brumbies would have scented us and our horses. It was surprising how, being on the site, we began to lock together the pieces of a pattern.

When Mick had scraped his diagrams in the dust back at the gilgii, he had marked only what any bushman's eye would have recorded. His ride through the area had been brief and quick. He had noticed the many brumbie tracks, seen the stockyards, and seen one waterhole—the one to the westward. A chance traveler at a later date had told him about the other one.

So now, Mick scratched his head with pleasure. He felt pleased with the way things were shaping; glad that he had won the toss. I was, too. The brumbie country I knew of was good but had no ready-made stockyards. We would have had to build them, and that takes a lot of time and work.

The other waterhole was somewhere in the tangle of broken country behind us. We had to find it. Mick's chance traveler had said that it was to the northeastward of the stockyards, about five miles as the bee flies. It was another seepage, basined in a sandstone gully, eroded by wind and time.

With this much knowledge printed in our minds, we headed northeastward until several well-trodden brumbie pads scarred the ground beneath us. Our loose horses quickly shuffled onto one. Mick and I jogged along behind, quite content to follow. Where the pads all finally converged would be the waterhole.

It proved to be a clear, hard-bottomed pool, deep enough to swim in if we had wanted to. But the unwritten law of the bush is that no man bathes in landlocked water. It may be muddy and scummy, fouled by different kinds of animals; but no true bushman would foul it with soap or human contact. Water is prized as something to drink, not swim in.

For the remainder of the day, we organized our camp for the hard-riding, hard-working days that lay ahead. On a good square mile of grassy plain close to the gully, we short-hobbled all of our horses except one. Around their necks we buckled "Condomine" horse bells. The clanging of these brass bells will carry over a distance of anything up to five miles if the wind is in the right direction. We relied on them to frighten away brumbie stallions, or at least give us warning if any came marauding, or to drive off our mares.

The one unhobbled horse we tethered near the camp. The idea was always to have one horse near at hand for an emergency. We fed it partly from the sack of oats we had bought from the storekeeper, partly with stacks of cut dried grass. Each horse in the herd would have a day and night turn on the picket rope.

Having solved the horse problem, we stripped our saddles down for greasing and inspection. A split girth or broken bridle rein can kill a man when he's racing over ground that sun and wind has cracked into a corrugated nightmare.

The hunted brumbies know every twist and turn of the pads along which they gallop. They never deviate, knowing full well that their safety lies in their knowledge. The hunter has to flog and spur across impossible country to get ahead of the flying brumbies in order to wheel them and drive them from their familiar tracks. It's only after this has happened that the chance comes to handle the galloping, mane-tossing animals.

Knowing all this, Mick and I worked thoroughly. Every suspect buckle was cut and restitched; every faulty strap or rein was replaced. By the time our saddles were reassembled, the sun gleamed redly on a dust-filled horizon. It was time to boil the billy and get our blankets unrolled for the night.

The next morning, before dawn's light, we strapped axes to our saddles and rode across to the stockyards. Close to them, we heard the high piercing challenge of a stallion driving his mares through the lignum, but saw neither hoof nor rump. Their fresh tracks and droppings showed they had grazed within two or three miles of our camp. We hoped the bells would keep them at that distance.

Stripped to the waist, we cut and trimmed twenty or thirty big saplings—sufficient to replace all the broken rails in the yards. The scrub timber was tough, and every ax blow jarred. Trees bred in harsh, dry soil have a toughness difficult to believe.

With our shirts folded as pads for our shoulders, we carried the rails around to their different positions. The yards covered a good two acres; having to replace only thirty rails at the most seemed to us quite a fair proposition. Whoever built the yards in the first place must have used several men, over a period of months.

By the end of a sweating sixteen-hour day, we had every rail replacement wired up in position. The sun had glared down, even when we were cutting the timber; the stringy, sparse-leaved trees had given us little shade. We were two weary, sun-blackened men when we rode the five miles back to camp.

After a meal of tinned meat and vegetables, a good night's sleep worked wonders. Morning found us with sore shoulders, but otherwise fit. The rails we had carried, over distances up to half a mile, weighed close to two hundredweight—enough to make anyone's shoulder ache. We reckoned a day's light work, stringing wire through the trees, would just about put us right.

It did. With the two half-mile coils of wire and stack

of empty sacks strapped on a packhorse, we again rode across to the stockyards. Tying one end of a coil to a corner of the stockyards near the gate, we paid out the wire along the timber. Wherever possible, we fastened it to trees; where not possible, we fastened the wire to stakes, which we cut and drove into the ground.

When the wire was strung over about a quarter of a mile, we dropped the remainder of the coil on the ground. We dumped the other coil down with it, then cut some of the sacks into narrow strips, and hung them along the wire.

We were all set to start our brumbies running, if and when we could manage to wheel a herd. Brumbies will face a bush fire rather than a length of wire with strange wisps of sack fluttering from it. To round off the day's work, we cut great heaps of stakes and stacked them near the wire coils.

We passed the next day quietly. In the early hours, we sweated leisurely over trimming some of our horses' hoofs. One or two that showed signs of being bare, we shod with sets of old shoes stowed in our pack bags. By the look of the country over which we intended to gallop, our horses' feet needed all the attention we could give them. Mick did the hoof trimming; I shaped and nailed on the shoes. It was late afternoon when I straightened my back after rasping down the last nail clinch.

Before stretching out, with our hats tipped over our eyes, to catch a little sleep, we tethered two of our best horses handy and fed them on oats. These we intended to ride on our first reconnoiter after brumbies. Mick chose a big, muscly brown gelding; I chose a flat-boned, hammerheaded bay. Both were surefooted— hard as the nails I had driven in their feet.

Close to midnight, under a star-crusted sky, I nudged Mick's deeply breathing ribs. It was time to go. While I fed the two softly nickering horses another hatful of oats, Mick boiled the billy. Hunkered down in the warm starlight, we drank scalding tea and listened to the crunch of jaws as the two geldings ate—the sweetest music known to any lonely horseman.

By the time we had sifted the last mugsful of tea grounds through our teeth, the horses had finished eating. With our saddles hoisted on our shoulders, Mick and I boot-scuffed toward the picketed nags. In a few snorting, hoof-stamping minutes, we had the saddles tossed over their backs and strained to a girth-burying tightness.

When Mick mounted, his horse crow-hopped away into the darkness; I could hear Mick's swearing voice grunt with every jar. My own hack behaved more sociably. I sat on him quietly until Mick's horse settled down. Jostling knee to knee, we rode away from the camp.

Taking our sense of direction from the stars, we rode for an hour or two, swinging in a wide arc around where we judged the stockyards to be. We wanted, at daybreak, to be well on the far side of the westward waterhole. There was a sandstone escarpment there, up which we intended to ride.

If we could reach the top before sunrise, we would be in a position, when the sun's rays lipped the horizon, to see a vast sweep of country; see, too, where the brumbie herds were feeding before they fled into the lignum to shelter for the day. If any seemed to be in a favorable position, we intended to try our luck with them; see whether we could yard them. In brumbie running you have to take your chances as they come. You can plan to a certain extent, but the final arbiter is the element of luck.

Once, during our long saddle-creaking night ride, we heard a brumbie mare squeal, and the lustful, amorous trumpeting of a stallion, intent on wooing. The sounds carried far in the warm night air. We estimated them as being some half mile away, in the region of the scrub timber clump. The sounds made us edgy; eager to take the bridle reins short in our hands and feel the wind whip in our faces.

Our sense of direction proved right. Half an hour before sunrise, we felt the lift of our horses' withers as they climbed the ribby escarpment. Sandstone rock gritted under their hoofs. On the flat, wind-scoured top, we dismounted to await the dawn's red-hazed coming.

When it did come, the sky was indescribable. Great streaks of blood-red fire pushed away the night. With our hats tipped forward over our eyes, we climbed back into the saddle, the better to see our surroundings. They were worth seeing.

The bush has printed many strong memories on my

mind, but none quite like that first morning on the sandstone escarpment. Every scarlet-tipped ridge, shadowed gully, and enormous stretch of purple-bathed plain stands out as sharply today as it did then. It is a memory I shall carry with me to the last saddling paddock.

As the red-tinted light grew stronger, we saw several herds of wild horses. One herd seemed to be grazing on the horizon, directly on top of a bloody tip of sun. Another strung out in the distances behind us, head to tail in a long line of shuffling horseflesh, already trotting for cover. And in front of us, a herd of twenty or thirty pawed in the mud or rump-nibbled each other, close to the waterhole.

Neither Mick nor I spoke. In one hat-jerking, hoof-scraping fraction of a second, we reined our horses around and spurred down the escarpment. Mick went one way; I went the other. Chips of sandstone kicked up from our horses' hoofs.

For a crazy fifty yards of down-going, my horse skidded, half on his hocks, half on his nose. When he straightened up for a headlong gallop toward the waterhole, I glanced across for Mick. He was clamped hard in the saddle, swaying to every jerk and swinging his long whip thong. The cracks rolled like rifle fire, echoing in the gullies. Two hundred yards apart, we raced at heart-thumping, saddle-jerking speed.

The brumbies surged up out of the waterhole. Through a haze of dust, I saw one shaggy-maned mare stumble, almost to her knees, as a great stallion savaged

her with his teeth. Then a thunder of hoofs smashed
back at us. The brumbies were off, packed tight in
confusion, pounding for the lignum. In close to their
sweating rumps, the stallion shrilled madly, driving
with his teeth.

On that hot dust-filled morning, Mick rode fantasti-
cally. He said afterwards that I did, too. Maybe I did.
But I give pride of place to Mick. He was on the side
closest to the lignum. Hat flattened back on his head,
he rode as no man I have ever seen before, or since.
Every time I hurtled up out of a gully or crashed
through scrub over a ridge, I'd see Mick away to the
left of me, flogging his heavy whip. My own rose and
fell until I thought my arm would break.

We had to keep those brumbies running; keep them
packed together in a knot of sweating tightness. Given
time to think, they would have split into small bands
of three or four and separated onto the many deep-
scarred pads leading into the lignum.

Gradually, Mick and I narrowed the distance down
between us until we were only twenty yards apart. The
brumbies were about the same distance ahead. Dust
from their flailing, pounding hoofs stung in our faces.
We could smell the rancid sweat, strong on the stallion's
hide.

The crucial test drew closer. Success or failure, in
our first mad spurt of brumbie running, lay in the thick
wall of lignum drawing rapidly nearer. We coiled our
whips and looped them on our shoulders. Two hands

down, we rocked in our straining saddles and rode with every skill we knew.

Foot by foot, yard by yard, we gained on the breath-whistling brumbies. The endurance of back country saddle horses, trained over countless miles of track, is incredible. Our horses strained with every work-toughened muscle, fought with every tendon; and they won.

Mick smashed through the first outlying clump of lignum; I followed him. The pencil-pointed leaves stung our faces; the thick, matted stems tore our boots from the stirrups, but we pulled no reins. Riding along the fringe of that thick mat of lignum, we kept the flare-nostriled, careering brumbies galloping on the outside.

Several times, with stomach-sickening floundering, my horse nearly crashed headlong. Iron-fisted for the moment, I kept his head up, lifting him by sheer strength of arm. I saw Mick do the same; saw him at one stage almost on the ground, hands locked on the bridle.

Then we were past the lignum. A stretch of rough, broken ground spread toward the stockyards. The high railed fences seemed to be drawing close, all too quickly. Headlong in a thunder of hoofs, the brumbies sensed our intentions; sensed where we intended to drive them. Massed in a block of sweating, mane-tangled horseflesh, they hammered on past the stockyards.

Spurring for a final effort, Mick and I slid the whips

from our shoulders again as we rode crazily on the side of the herd. Under the whips' machine-gun crackling, the brumbies began to falter.

Out of my sweat-filled eyes, I saw the great stallion redouble his efforts, biting with savage teeth to keep the mares and young horses from turning. But he lost the fight. The fear of man grew stronger in the mares' brains than their fear of the stallion. They began to veer away to the right, still madly galloping, but swinging from their straight, headlong course.

I saw Mick backhand a fist, wiping sweat from his face, then jerk his hat tighter. We were in for the final test. Having overshot the yards, we had to drive the herd around in a wide circle. Part of the way would be through the far side of the scrub timber clump, then around to face up to the yards again, with the strip-hung wire acting as a wing on one side of the herd.

Legs braced to our rocking saddles, we drove the flying brumbies with every nerve we had. Our horses were tiring. The weight they were carrying, and the rough country over which they traveled, had to take its toll.

Several times I felt my own horse labor when he ripped up out of a gully or slid down a steep slope. Each time he did, his breathing sobbed in his throat; but his big hammerhead held steady. The small, pointed ears, set in their sweaty bases, stayed pricked. Eagerness to wheel the brumbies glared in his straining eyes.

When we pounded over a ridge into the far side of

the timber clump, sweat almost blinded me. Through a raw, hazed blur, I saw the brumbies twisting and turning, smashing down young saplings.

Mick was still just ahead of me, set tight in his saddle, but his horse was tired—more tired than mine. I could tell that by the way the gelding rolled as it answered to the rein. Yet, like my own hammerheaded bay, the big gelding fought on gamely, determined to die on its feet rather than give in. And the brumbies were tiring, too. Great scuds of frothing sweat foamed on their jostling flanks. Their iron-hard hoofs began to pound uncertainly.

Smashing clear of the timber, the wild herd whinnied toward the lignum, again eager for its shelter. But our horses held them; turned them toward the stockyards. In a final burst of madly drumming hoofs, we wheeled them toward the gates. From there on, Mick and I rode like madmen, holding up our horses by sheer will-power.

At one stage, the great stallion ripped at every rump near him, trying to drive the herd into the timber. But the sight of the fluttering single-strand wire proved too much. The brumbies turned again and headed for the gates.

If I had to live that wild, fantastic ride over again, I would cheerfully do it, except for one part—the last one hundred yards. It was a nightmare of tired, weary uncertainty, overshadowed by a blazing sun. If the brumbies had made one last concerted effort and surged away from the stockyards, Mick and I could never have stopped them. We could neither have raised our whips nor urged our horses to another gallop; they were too tired.

In the manner of things, perhaps defined by fate or the luck given to men who try, the brumbies galloped straight. They raced through the gateway, into the big, many-sectioned yards. A great smother of dust billowed out through the rails.

Reining our horses down to their haunches, Mick and I literally fell from their backs. We had to. Urgency kicked us up from the dust, and we ran toward the gates. Mick slammed one half; I slammed the other.

I had barely twisted the heavy chain twice around the two halves before the brumbies came galloping back, the big stallion in the lead. His teeth grated on a metal strap just above my hand as I shackled the last chain link. Another precious second and we would have lost the herd—every last hoof and sweating hair of them.

As it was, they drummed around the yards in another effort to find a way out. They made several attempts to jump the seven-foot-high fences, while Mick and I unsaddled our horses.

With the tired animals slouching behind us, we walked toward the waterhole. It was a long, hot, dusty walk over part of the same ground on which we had recently galloped, but it gave us a chance to stretch our legs. At the same time, the slow walk, without tight girths around their briskets, helped the two geldings to steady their laboring ribs.

When we reached the waterhole, our sweaty hats served as buckets to dip water. Standing on a sandstone ledge, we took it in turns to wash the horses from nose tip to tail end.

Before letting the horses drink, Mick and I stretched out flat on our backs for an hour or two. It is dangerous to allow horses to drink when they are hot; it founders them quickly.

When we judged their condition was right, we let the horses drink, but only a few mouthfuls. Neither Mick nor I drank. We were strictly midday and sundown men; the rest of the day, if we were too dry, we sucked a pebble. It can be a great help.

Looping the bridle reins over our arms, we led the renewed and now satin-coated geldings back to the stockyards.

The brumbies still churned restlessly, and a heavy pall of dust hung over the yards while we resaddled. Mounting quickly, we trotted away. We judged it best to leave the snorting, wild-eyed horses alone for at least a day; give them a chance to settle and become accustomed to being encircled by the yards. We were not even sure just how many we had trapped. All we did know was that they seemed to be fairly decent types of animal, with one sure "snag" amongst them— the stallion.

For the remainder of the day, Mick and I discussed the pros and cons of our next move, or moves. We had the brumbies in the yard. Now we had to get them out again; drive them across country for possibly several hundred miles. We thought we could manage it by giving them a little schooling first; stringing our wire around in a great circle and "running" the brumbies inside it, with our own horses acting as steadiers.

The one drawback to doing this was, of course, the stallion. He was liable to do anything, not the least of which would be savaging our horses; ripping them to pieces. We had three days at the most to work fast in. That was the limit to which the horses could be held without water. Bred under harsh conditions, as they were, they could last that long.

We could have shot the stallion out of hand, but neither of us wanted to. We knew he was dangerous, yet, as Mick said, in one of his head-scratching moments of philosophy, he was "as God made him."

Finally, we decided to quickly break the stallion, then put a muzzle and various other aids to quietness on him. In this manner we hoped we might be able to control him sufficiently. The stars clung close to the sky when Mick and I rolled up in our blankets. The next day held great possibilities of being eventful.

Dawn found us mounted on fresh horses, carrying our breaking-in gear. Arriving at the stockyards, we were greeted with a medley of drumming hoofs and nervous, flare-nostriled snorting, high above which pealed the wild call of the stallion. His day and night in the yards had not improved his temper. In fact, it had worsened.

He slammed his rock-hard hoofs on the rails directly in front of us as we slid from our saddles. I had brought a rifle in case of accidents, and laid it on the ground under a bottom rail. By the way the stallion was behaving, I began to think we were sure to need it.

Valor has no place in horsemanship. Every bad horse you ride or handle sets the nerves tingling down your spine; gives you a hollow, tight-gutted feeling. It's one of those occupations where you are entirely on your own—skill against brute strength. And a wild bush stallion has enormous muscular strength.

The long, thin stockwhip Mick coiled in his hand, as he climbed through the rails, seemed puny. I followed him, with a whip in one hand and a greenhide lasso in the other. Our intentions were to drive the stallion into a small round pen, set in the middle of the stockyards.

Head to heel behind Mick, I was still bent double as the stallion leaped. Mick was prepared, but his legs were stiff, as mine were, from the previous day's hard riding. He wasn't quite quick enough. His feet stumbled as the stallion's yellow teeth champed past his ear. The brute's big jowls smashed the side of Mick's face, knocking him sprawling. His head split on a post as he hit the ground. Over the top of my own startled skull, I heard the brute's two hoofs slam sickeningly. The whole of the fence shuddered.

Tangled mane and tail streaming, the wild stallion plunged away. At a distance of about twenty yards, he wheeled to charge back again. Struggling to get to Mick, I had barely time to see the great body arc up and over. His heavy chest struck the top rail, tipping him over in a complete somersault.

He smashed down on the other side of the fence, almost on top of my saddle horse. The two rolled on the ground in a tangle of hoofs and grunting bodies. And, as I had expected, the stallion stamped up to his feet, with his vicious teeth clamped to my saddle horse's neck.

For a sweating, groping second, I fumbled with the rifle. Stretched over Mick's unmoving legs, I brought the sights into alignment with the brute's great chest. As I gently squeezed the trigger, I heard my saddle horse squeal pitifully. Then he again slumped to the ground as the stallion's death struggles dragged him down.

Within one or two minutes at the most, Mick had been knocked out cold, the stallion shot dead, and my saddle horse frightened out of its wits. Such are the chances of brumbie running.

Once more my saddle horse struggled up to its feet, this time to stand shaking its neck. Bent over Mick, I examined his head as best I could. The sweaty yellowness of his face scared me for a moment, but he seemed to be breathing all right. Little bubbles of froth showed on his mouth corners.

When I rolled him over, the cut on the back of his head bled freely. As far as I could tell, no part of his cranium was broken. I dragged him out under the rails and stripped off my shirt, tucking it under his head for a pillow.

My next problem was water. I had to have some to clean Mick's wound and try to bring him around. The nearest to hand—and I had only my hat to carry it in— was the westward lying waterhole. All our gear was at the camp, five miles away.

I wasted no time. In the bush, a man gets used to doing things the hard way. Mounted on Mick's horse, I flogged to the waterhole and back in record time. When I skidded to a halt, close to Mick's bloody head, I heard him groaning. He was already coming around.

From there on it was simple bush first-aid. I tipped half the precariously carried hatful of water into Mick's face, to wash away the sweat and dust, then bathed the gaping split with the remainder. I had added Condy's crystals from my saddlebags to make the water antiseptic. There is always a risk of tetanus infecting cuts sustained in a stockyard, but I couldn't do anything about that.

In a matter of minutes Mick was sitting up, nursing his head in his hands. When he could speak, the first question he asked me was, had I caught the stallion.

I waited till he looked at me, then jerked a silent thumb. It was enough. The big carcass, sprawled close to our saddle horses, told its own story. Mick lowered his head and rested it back on his arms. He must have had a shocking headache.

After he had staggered to his feet, with some aid from me, I hoisted him up onto his saddle and climbed into my own. We forgot about the remainder of the brumbies for the moment. It was more important to get Mick across to our camp, where we had plenty of water. The gash on the back of his head was serious; it would have put many men in hospital for a fortnight.

As for my saddle horse, he was slightly ripped on the neck, but had come to no great harm. He would live to gallop another day. Mick's head was the pressing problem.

Arriving at the camp, I clipped hair from Mick's head with a pair of horse clippers. With water boiled in the billy, and another pinch of Condy's crystals, I thoroughly cleaned the cut, gouging out most of the embedded dirt with a new shoeing nail, boiled in the water.

By the time I finished, the cut looked a deep, rich crimson, perfectly free of all debris. I began to fancy myself as a surgeon—although Mick's language tended to show a different opinion on the score. To complete the job, I strapped one of the new horse bandages around his head, squeezing the edges of the cut in together. The whole was quite a fair effort.

We boiled the billy for tea and had a few hours' spell before riding back to the stockyards. Although the sun was pouring down a fantastic heat, Mick rode without a hat—he couldn't get it on over the thick roll of bandage.

For the rest of the afternoon we drove stakes into the sunbaked ground to form a wide semicircle in front of the stockyards, then strung the remainder of the wire, with strips of sack hanging from it.

The area enclosed was a good square quarter of a mile—sufficient for us to gallop the brumbies about in, if needed. What we had to hope for was a fairly strong wind to keep the sack strips fluttering.

That night, throughout the hot breathless hours, Mick tossed and groaned restlessly. Ear cocked in the darkness, I debated several times whether to ride to Yancannia—to get a conveyance to come out for him. But when daylight broke, Mick crawled out of his blankets, ready to go to work. Screw-eyed over a pannikin of tea, he said he felt fine; fit to ride any brumbie ever foaled. There's nothing you can do with a man like that except climb up into a saddle and ride with him—which I did.

Luck was with us to a certain extent when we reached the stockyards. A scorching westerly came suddenly bowling, as is the custom of westerlies, and drove great gusts of dust before it. The sack strips on the wire fluttered in pennants of fury, ready to keep any brumbies at a distance. I rubbed a stubbled chin. Mick did the same. We spat in our hands before we opened the gates.

The brumbies came out in a flood, with Mick and myself galloping in front of them. Around and around inside the fluttering circle we galloped, trotted, walked, swore, and cursed; then did it all over again. Hour after sweating, cursing hour, until finally the brumbies broke into a compact, controllable herd. Then we drove them back into the yards and slammed the gates.

Several times during the morning, I noticed Mick

almost reach a point of no return in the saddle. Each time, with an effort known only to himself, he forced his body upright; kept his legs clamped tight to the leather.

In the late evening, we ran the brumbies again. For a few hectic minutes, they repeated their morning's performance, but we quickly controlled them. Mick's sweaty face cracked in a grin when we reyarded them.

We bumped stirrup to stirrup riding back to camp, pleased with our success and eager for a meal. We had been all day with the brumbies, even in the stockyards, after we had finished running them. They were now fairly used to us. There were nineteen mares and fifteen youngsters; a total of thirty-four head.

During the night the wind died to a dust-filled whisper. Mick had another restless, twisting sleep, yet when I stirred at daybreak, he pulled on his boots the same time that I did. After a billy of tea and a tin of pork and beans, we stripped the hobbles from our loose horses, then drove them across to the stockyards. Inside the wire, I held them while Mick swung open the gates.

The next half hour or so was another sweating, swearing repetition of the previous morning. Luckily again, the whisper of wind was sufficient to keep the strips flapping. The brumbies made no attempt to break through.

In the manner of men who know what they are doing, we brought them to a halt, clustered around our own horses. So far, so good. Our first attempt at educating the brumbies to stand in the open met with success.

Their shaggy necks were still undaunted, but their fiery eyes were losing their savage glow.

I have always thought that much of the fear and wildness inherent in brumbie herds is caused by the great bush stallions—brutes who survive by savagery of hoof and ripping, tearing teeth. Even mares are at times battered to death by them. It takes months, or perhaps a year or more, to thoroughly quiet a brumbie mare or gelded youngster—but it can be done. A brumbie stallion remains a brumbie—and a killer.

For the remainder of the day, we jog-shuffled the herd for interminable miles around and around the enclosed area. Toward late afternoon, with the westering sun's strong glare in our eyes, we licked our dusty lips before deciding to take a chance—open the wire and drive the herd to the waterhole; give them a drink before shutting them in the stockyards for the night. It was a little earlier than we had planned, but we thought that with our own horses to act as steadiers, we could manage it.

An old, saddle-bowed man once said to me, when we were breaking in together, "Never give way to kindness. Keep the hand firm; the voice steady; and the heart where it ought to be—inside your shirt."

With freshly saddled horses under us, Mick and I cut the wire and rode out through the gap. We expected, or half expected, that the brumbies, being thirsty, would head straight for the waterhole. Anxious-eyed while we waited to steady them, we watched them surge toward the gap. One second they were inside it;

the next, they were out in a jostling tangle of manes, galloping for the lignum, with our own loose horses heading sedately for the water.

Once again Mick and I sat down in our saddles. Rocking, swaying, swearing, cursing, we crashed into gullies; hoof-smashed up over ridges; belly-flattened down on sun-cracked claypans. Through a haze of blinding dust, choking up in our slit-eyed faces, we saw the lignum draw closer, the brumbies pound, in a welter of hoofs and tails. Then we spurred past them; wheeled them around toward the waterhole, with our whips flogging a wild tattoo.

At sight of our loose horses drinking quietly, hock-deep in the water, the brumbies steadied; skidded to a hoof-scraping halt. Mick and I had again beaten them— but only just. We sat on our panting horses, wiping the sweat from our eyes; sick, for the moment, of brumbies, dust, and the hot sun glaring down on our backs.

Full flanked from their drink, the brumbies snorted up from the waterhole, ready for another gallop. Mick and I, too, were ready. Hands low on our bridles, we drove them, tight-bunched with our own loose horses, back to the stockyards. We were tired men when we slammed the gates. Mick nearly fell from his saddle. He had to rest, with his shoulders against a post, before we could ride across to our camp.

Dawn found us awake, bent over our pack bags. We threw away every nonessential in order to lighten the loads. When we started across country, the packhorses would have to travel far and fast in order to keep up with the brumbies. With pack and saddle horses tightly girthed, we rode for the last time toward the stock-yards, urging our cavalcade in front of us.

When we opened the gates, the brumbies made a concerted charge toward the lignum; but the fire had left them. Under the control of the two fast, spin-turn-ing stock horses Mick and I had saved for the last, they snorted into submission. Bunched with our own horses, we started them on the way out.

For days—sometimes nights—we seemed to ride end-lessly, changing our saddle horses two or three times a day. Where there was a set of stockyards or a "Govern-ment Reserve" paddock, we camped; where not, we pushed on.

We were two lean, narrow-belted "saddle bashers" when we met a lone horseman. Over a billy of tea, he told us the latest bush gossip, then spoke about a horse dealer he had heard was somewhere to the northward. The dealer was traveling with a "mob" of six hundred, on his way down to Bourke, or further "in" to Parkes.

Mick and I crawled back into our saddles. After three or four days, following fresh directions from different travelers, we shaded our eyes to see a big mob of horses grazing on the skyline.

When we drew close, we saw the smoke of a camp-fire under some stunted trees. A few men were squatted, eating; others were scattered far, riding slowly around the grazing horses. Near an orderly stack of pack-saddles, a big man sat on his own. We could see him, hat tipped over his face, staring at us. He was the dealer.

Leaving Mick to "hold" our horses, I rode over to do the initial skirmishing. Hands knuckled on the pommel, I nodded down at the big man and said the usual good day. He nodded back. Not a line creased on his tough, craggy face. Then I told him he had a nice lot of horses; there were some "good sorts" amongst them.

For one who had just had a hurried glance at the fringe of some six hundred horses, this wasn't a bad effort. The dealer seemed to think so, too. He squinted one eye and spat through his teeth. Finally, I told him I had thirty-four head of mares, colts, and fillies for a sale. If he was interested, would he ride out with me and look at them?

Mounted on a heavy, bald-faced bay, he rode beside me to where Mick sat, slouched in his saddle. After the usual nods, the dealer rode slowly through our herd, inspecting the now more or less docile, road-weary brumbies. There was no need to point them out to him; they were "cleanskins," or unbranded, still shaggy-maned and tailed.

When he reined over to face us, the dealer folded his hands, resting them on the pommel. Without twitching an eyelid, he made us an offer—take it or leave it. It was a reasonable offer, but less than we had expected.

Mick dug in his pockets for a penny. I called heads; he called tails. One of us had to win.

We sold our brumbies. With his checkbook resting on his saddle, the dealer wrote a check, making it out to cash.

The last we saw of our brumbies, they were merged in the great herd of horses drifting toward the horizon.

Yumpin' Yarley

When the phone rang, I was bandaging my big toe. A horse had trodden on it the previous day, and I could barely walk. In fact, the whole previous week seemed to have been filled with trouble. Small troubles, perhaps, but enough to make me wary as I lifted the receiver.

The voice I heard was Jack Julian's. He was my nearest neighbor, on a property some twenty miles away.

"Come over," Jack said, "and give us a hand. I'm branding cattle tomorrow. Five hundred bullocks from the Territory."

Then he went on to tell me the cattle would be in the yards near his homestead. After talking to me, he was "off out, to take delivery of 'em from a Territory drover."

I listened to him talk and felt more trouble was near. Northern Territory cattle are always touchy, even after a long road trip. Yet you have to help a neighbor.

"Sure," I said. "I'll be over at daylight. Have the billy on when I get there; otherwise, I'll miss out on breakfast."

Jack was pleased. "Yeah," his voice crackled. "And a steak on the coals. See yer, Reg."

Then he hung up, leaving me to my bandaging.

For the rest of the day I lived quietly. I was on my own at the time, looking after a property. In the evening, I shut a night-horse in the stalls, ready for an early start.

The next morning, true to my word, I arrived at the stockyards at daybreak. True to his, Jack had a steak on the coals. While I wolfed it down, followed by great gulps of tea, Jack squatted beside me. The rest of his men stood, or sat, near the fire—except one, who was chopping wood. He was a Swede—short and powerfully built. At one time he'd jumped ship in Sydney and made his way to the bush. Jack had given him a job as a general rouseabout, but he never made the grade as a bushman. He'd get lost in the scrub or carve his leg with an ax. Yet we all liked him. You couldn't help doing so. Under his thick blond hair, his face held a look of permanent surprise.

"By yimminy," he'd say, if he fell off a horse. "By yumpin' yarley."

So, out of principle, we called him Yarley.

After I had eaten, Jack straightened his legs.

"Right," he said. "Now we'll do some work. You do the branding, Reg. I'll earmark. The rest of yer know what t' do."

As one man, we plodded across to the big sprawl of ramshackle yards and the bawling bullocks inside them.

Still sore-toed, I was glad Jack had given me the branding. I would be up above the great, heavy-railed crush, on a narrow boardwalk. After someone tossed me the hot iron, I'd brand, then toss the iron back. There would be no one to tread on my foot, and I wouldn't have to work the constant relays of cattle needed in the crush. It held about twenty head of tightly packed bullocks. As the last one was branded, the forward gates would be opened, and the crush emptied. Then it would be refilled.

Like all stockwork where you deal with large numbers, the work has to be fast and efficient. Freshly bought cattle may have the brands of several previous owners on them. The new one you put on has to be legible and stand out clearly. Men have gone to jail for wrongly branded cattle.

Be that as it may, I had time to look around as I climbed up onto my "bird" walk. Below me, some few yards from the crush, smoldered two fire buckets. Yarley was in charge of them and already had the branding irons heating. He was bent over, stoking more wood on the fires.

Beyond and around, in the various holding yards, the restless, nervy cattle bawled. Bred on a vast Northern Territory "run," they looked to be six-year-olds, big, rawboned fellows, with great ribby frames. You could see their horns glitter.

When we were settled in our places, Jack gave the word to start. Two of his men on horseback cut off a wing of cattle and drove them into the forcing yards. From there again, some twenty head were drafted by men on foot and driven into the crush. As the last tail-swishing animal scrambled in, the gate was forced shut behind it. From there on, the two men on foot slipped through a small safety gate, then hurried forward to be ready to release the cattle.

Jack began earmarking. High on the bird walk, I yelled for a branding iron. Yarley tossed one. I caught it, then pressed it on a bullock. There's a rhythm about branding that has a fascination. Toss, catch, bend, and brand; toss back again, as you straighten. It's a job that has to be done, so the thing to do is do it as quickly as possible.

I learned in a hard school, under some tough men. But Yarley was inclined to get flustered. He was supposed to catch a returned brand with one hand and toss a fresh one with the other. More often than not, he had two hot brands in one hand at once, or was jumping sideways to dodge a flying iron. Yet we managed—though I could feel the blisters beginning to form on my palms. It's one of the problems you face if the irons are not tossed right. Some branders wear a glove, but the glove gets hot. You still get the blisters.

Every pause for a fresh crushful, Yarley wiped his streaming face. Being so blond, he turned a raw, fiery red.

"By yimminy," I heard him say, while fresh bullocks

87

surged into the crush. "By yumpin' yarley. Vere is dis end for stoppin'?" I guessed he meant when would the branding end.

Most of the morning, the work flowed along smoothly. We had the odd mishaps, but nothing serious. Knocks are expected in cattle work and taken as they come. They're part of a job, which is one of the last rough, tough occupations. For myself, I felt that having survived some of Yarley's worst shots, the jinx had left my shoulder. All that remained was to see the job through.

But toward noon, Yarley stepped backward and knocked over a fire bucket. It had to be righted and the brands reset. While we waited for them to heat, Yarley asked for a change of jobs. He said his hands were too sore to catch or throw another brand. They did look sore when he held them out to Jack for inspection. Ridged, swollen skin bubbles had burst on his palms.

I nodded as Jack glanced at me. The way I saw it, no one could be worse. Besides, Yarley needed a break. You could see he was really worried.

"Sure," I said. "Go ahead and change him. Most of 'em's done, so why worry."

There were, at the time, about another hundred to do. It looked a reasonable gamble.

Jack scratched his ear. He knew Yarley better than I did.

"OK," he finally said. "You can help crush 'em, Yarley. Joe can do the brands." And he turned away, as if to say, "Well, there it is. Don't blame me for what happens."

Yarley was pleased. I expect that, somewhere along the line, he'd hankered to be a cowboy.

"T'anks," he said. "I crush 'em all right. By yumpin' yarley, yes."

Jack was back near the crush when he drawled, "Yeah. Well see that ya' do some yumpin'."

From there on, we settled down to the routine again.

For the first crushful, Yarley seemed to manage fairly well. The man with him helped him along, and in the speed of the work, Yarley was forgotten. At odd times, when I glanced down, he was either spitting on his hands or rubbing them in dust.

Then a following crushful seemed more troublesome than most. That's the way it happens in a big mob of cattle. You get a string of really rowdy bullocks all together at once. No one can explain why, but there it is.

And again, in the scheme of events, the time was due for someone to be careless—or for a gate catch not to work properly. Whatever the cause, the rear gate of the crush wasn't fastened securely.

As I branded the last bullock, it floundered backward. Its bony rump pressed for a moment, then the gate burst open. The bullock sprawled head over hocks into the forcing yard. On the opposite side, Yarley was just getting ready to unchain another gate, ready to drive in more cattle.

At a time like that, you seem to register every movement. The man forward slammed open his gates to empty the crush. Jack began running, with a notebook in his hand. I stood upright, with a branding iron in mine.

Down in the forcing yard, Yarley just stood. I guess his legs had frozen. Struggling up from the dust, the bullock snorted, chokingly. In one quick glance, you could see the whole, yet feel you were disbelieving.

The bullock moved first. Angry from the brand, it ripped straight at Yarley. I saw it skid, plowing into the gate, but Yarley wasn't there. Some way or other, he'd found the strength to move, though he hadn't time to climb.

The bullock wheeled and bumped Yarley away from the fence. I saw his dazed, puzzled eyes blink before he fell headlong. The next moment I was in the yard myself. Don't ask me why, but there I was, sore toe and all.

"Get up," I yelled, "and climb. He's got his eye on me."

That was an understatement. He had more than his eye. The whole big, rawboned hulk of him came straight at me. I hit him on the nose with the brand, then jumped for the fence. As I pulled myself up to the top rail, I felt the bullock snort behind me.

For extra impetus, I jerked on the rail, and it broke. Out of all the rails in that great spread of stockyards, I'd picked probably the only rotten one. Weathered and worn, it snapped in the middle. I fell on the bullock's head.

But my luck had changed. The brute was cock-horned; one horn turned up, the other turned down. The upturned one skewered a thin red streak up the back of my leg and tore my trousers. The other was the one I fell on.

With an almighty bellow, the bullock tossed me cleanly. The high fence was feet below me as I hurtled over, then landed quietly, spread flat, on the other side.

When I did sit up, I looked around for Yarley. He'd climbed out safely. The bullock had the yard to himself. Jack leaned on the crush, looking down at me.

"Of all the fool things," he said, "yours beats the best. I thought he had you."

I straightened the leg of my trousers.

"Yeah," I said. "I thought he had, too."

Then we went on with the branding.

Midnight

I had been traveling for a month when I rode into Yackembah, a big station on the borders of New South Wales. The season wasn't too good; neither were my horses. The two of them were as nipped in at the flanks as a greyhound on racing day. I wasn't in much better shape, either. The hot sun had pared me down to a framework. Every time I tightened my belt, the buckle scraped on my backbone. The three of us needed somewhere to rest up for a while. Yackembah looked as good a place as any. So I kept my fingers crossed when I walked into the office to have a yarn with the owner, Ken Russell.

After we had yarned about the weather, and things in general, he offered me a job breaking in half a dozen young horses. This suited me fine. Ken made no time limit. I reckoned if I spun the job out, my horses would have a chance to fatten; maybe get the weariness out of their legs. At the same time, I had the thought that I might put a little padding where my own stomach was supposed to be. Having worked all that out, it didn't take me long to sign a contract.

The next week or two passed pleasantly. I handled three or four of the youngsters, and they behaved themselves well. One tried kicking me when I put my boot in the stirrup. Another threw himself over backward, with me on his back. Apart from that, they gave no trouble. The padding I'd hoped for began to push out my belt buckle. In a distant paddock, my own horses began to look sleek. As far as I was concerned, not a cloud showed on the skyline.

Then Ken brought up the matter of Midnight. At the time, Ken was sitting on the top rail of the stockyards. I was down inside, riding a colt. In between crow-hopping grunts and snorts from my horse, I heard Ken telling me Midnight's history. It didn't sound promising.

Midnight's mother had been an outlaw who'd flattened more riders in the dust than a man could count. She had also been bad. By that, I mean she was vicious. Once she'd thrown you, she'd try to trample on you; tread you into the ground. She had finally killed herself. But not, of course, before Midnight was born.

Midnight had a further splotch on his pedigree. He was the result of a chance mating between the mare and a brumbie stallion. When you added it all up, Midnight's chance of becoming a lady's hack didn't seem too good. Yet what lived in Ken's mind was Midnight himself—never mind his history. Ken reckoned he was one of the finest horses he'd ever seen. Big crested; jet black; not a white marking on him. You could feel a horseman's love for good horseflesh when Ken said it.

I scraped with my spurs for a buck or two longer, then unsaddled. While Ken put away the saddle, I cleaned down the colt. When I'd put him in another yard, Ken and I sat under a tree to work out the pros and cons of Midnight. The trouble was, he was seven years old. In my experience, a horse of that age, even with everything in his favor, seldom breaks into a good horse.

Finally, we tossed up. Heads, I'd have a crack at breaking him; tails, Ken would shoot him. The penny seemed a long time going up. When it came down, it showed heads. Midnight had a reprieve; but you couldn't have said for how long.

The next morning I saddled a night-horse while the sky was still gray. Even the kookaburras hadn't laughed themselves off their perches. Once away from the stock-yards, I had about six square miles of country to search in for Midnight.

I found him after an hour or so. He was grazing with a mob of mixed horses—something like thirty-odd head. And when they saw me, you'd have thought they were brumbies. Before I could spit on my hands to get a good grip on the reins, they were off, flat to the boards— every last tail-switching one of 'em.

In a welter of hoofs and dust, they flogged it for the horizon, with me after them, carving it out in the wind. For a good cursing, spurring half mile, they nearly beat me. Then I wheeled 'em, brought them around under the whip, and headed them for home.

With the great spread of plains stretched out before us, we thundered in the wildest ride you ever saw. My horse loved it. So did I. And so did the mob. You could smell the sweat glistening on their rippling bodies, hear their snorting breath, and see the great power of their pounding rumps. My horse had to strain every muscle to stay up with them; but he made it. No matter how they tried to twist and turn, he was there, ready to head 'em. It was the sort of ride you wished would go on forever.

When the stockyards showed, Ken was crouched on the rails, ready to slam the gates. As the last half mile cut down to yards, Midnight fought for the lead. In a tangle of flying manes, he hammered for every yard. His great hoofs pounded until I thought they'd split. Then he hurtled through the gates. In a tossing column of dust, the rest followed him. Close to their streaming tails, Ken slammed the gates. They were home—but not dried. The sweat was dripping from their bellies.

While the dust was settling, I unsaddled my hack. From the way he behaved, you would have thought he was crazy. But that's the way plains-bred horses are. They love a gallop. The great distances breed it in 'em. By the time I'd got the saddle off him, he'd trodden on my foot and generally made a fool of himself. I slapped him on the rump and let him go. He finished up rolling on his back, kicking his legs.

Back in the yards, Ken and I drafted the horses;

some one way, some another. Finally, only the black ebony of Midnight was left. He stood in the far corner of the yard, alone, in a swirl of dust. It was the first time I had seen him properly at close quarters.

He was all that Ken had said. If anything, he was more. From Ken's description, I'd been able to spot him that morning, but no words could describe his character or bearing. You had to see him for yourself. When you did, you got a shock. Not only was he big, in a heavy-crested way, but he'd a head that flared with dominance.

Be that as it may, you can't sit on a fence forever. Someone has to fire the first shot—only in this case, the shot was a rope I tossed over Midnight's neck.

As it settled, Ken and I braced ourselves for the shock. Nothing happened. Just that. Nothing at all. By all the rules of bush horsemanship, Midnight should have fought until his eyes bulged; or he should have charged and tried to trample us in the dust. He did neither. Not an ear flattened. Not a muscle twitched. Not an eyelid quivered.

Ken sweated in the palms. So did I. There's something not right about a horse who behaves like that—especially when he's unbroken, seven years old, and bred from brumbie stock.

However, once a rope's tossed, you have to follow on. While Ken rubbed his hands in the dust to get a better grip, I fetched a halter. After a few stealthy hand movements around Midnight's head, I slipped the halter over his ears. Again no movement. You would have thought he'd worn a halter every day of his life.

By then, Ken was really worried.

"Watch him, Reg," he kept saying. "Watch him. This horse is a killer. He's waiting on you."

I told him he needn't worry. I'd much the same notion. If I watched any harder, my eyes would burst.

The next step was to lead Midnight; teach him to follow a rope. At least, that was the general idea. But again, things didn't follow their normal course.

Behind the stables we kept a big horse for special jobs. After I had saddled him, I buckled a strap around his neck, then rode him into the yard. Ken passed me Midnight's halter lead. I hitched it in the strap. From there on, I reckoned it would be every man for himself.

As the big horse moved off, I jammed my feet in the stirrups, waiting for the impact. There wasn't any. Just one or two tugs, then Midnight followed along without trouble. His heavy body scrubbed against my leg. I reached over and patted him.

There's no sense in spinning out a yarn. It's good enough to say the rest of Midnight's breaking followed the same pattern. I put a roller and crupper on him; mouthed him; picked up his feet. He did it all as if he'd done it before. A little stiffly, perhaps, but he did it. I worked on him all day. The next morning I gave him a freshener. In the afternoon, he was ready for riding.

Any station-bred horse, when you ride him for the first time, is an unknown quantity. You're never quite sure what he's going to do; what his special brand of mischief will be. Whether he'll kick, bite, or buck; or whether he'll throw himself over backward and flatten you in the dust. It's just one of those things. You have to climb on his back to find out. That's how I felt about Midnight.

I'd already got to like him, but Ken didn't feel the same. You could tell that when he saddled a horse and rode into the yard, to be with me. If ever a man's chin sagged on his chest, Ken's did. He said afterwards he was pretty sure I was in for a rough ride. He had a feeling he might have to scrape me off the rails or maybe straighten out a leg.

Ken held Midnight's head while I saddled him. In the manner of the outback, I buried the girths deep. You have to. If the saddle slips, you've got a dinghy's chance in a cyclone. When the saddle was right, I nudged a boot into the stirrup.

On that hot, sunny afternoon, you could've heard an ant cough. Ken stopped breathing. So did I. Midnight stood still. I pressed a knee into Midnight's shoulder and slid quietly into the saddle. Everything for a thousand miles, including Midnight, stood still.

I let him get the feel of me, then poked him around the stockyard. He moved on oiled springs. You could feel the power pumping through him as his hoofs whispered on the dust. After a round or two, I told Ken to open the gate; he was right. We'd take him out where we could carve up a bit of distance.

Ken opened the gate, and out we went. No fuss. No

bother. No snorting or shying. Just a slow, gentle walk. It was grand. Not a cloud blemished the sky.

Ken was just telling me what a surprise Midnight had been when the sky came down. Midnight balled into the craziest buck I've ever scraped spurs on. For a long split second, he seemed to be clawing at the sun. When he came down, the jar was out of this world. Every tooth I had jumped. But not as hard as Midnight. He went up again, and from there on, it's hazy. Just one of the things you read about. Or do you? I don't think it's in a book. If it is, it must be the one Midnight threw at me.

In a heaving, groaning mass, he bucked, twisted, and spun; even went down on his knees to roll on me. Before I could hook him up out of it, he'd already pinned one of my legs. But I rode him.

Finally, he smashed his head around to bite me. It was the last line in the book. I kicked his teeth away with the stirrup, then reefed on the reins. How I'd made the grade, I don't know. But I still had a kneeful of saddle. Midnight was right there, underneath it.

After I had straightened him out, I headed Midnight for the horizon, with Ken spurring behind. There's one thing about the plains country; you've got plenty of room. By the time we headed back to the stockyards, Midnight was ready to call it a day. So was I. Another half hour on that saddle, and I'd never have brought my legs together again.

Early the next morning, I climbed onto Midnight again. I thought I'd get him out and away before anyone was about. The way it had been the day before, I knew there hadn't been much in it. Another twist or two after he'd tried to bite my leg would have had me spurring in the air. I reckoned if Midnight was going to splatter me in the dust, I didn't want anybody to see it happen. You know how it is. A man gets like that at times.

It was the same story all over again. We went out through the gates with no trouble. Midnight padded quietly, barely stirring the dust. But it had to come. When I leaned over from his back to unlatch a gate, he nearly had me. I tore the skin off my legs, fighting to stay with him. He ripped and spun for a good half acre. Then he stopped. Just like that. I could have poured a bucket of oats down his neck. Instead, we flogged away on another wild gallop.

That's the way it went, right along the line. I rode him more or less every day for some two months. I finished off the other half-dozen youngsters and passed them out to the men. They became good, quiet hacks. But Midnight never changed. I tried every trick I knew, from kindness to downright toughness. It made no difference. He bucked once every day. If it was possible, his technique improved. So did mine. I learned more from Midnight than any other horse. And at the last buck, he always had me hanging on by my eye-lashes—or I thought he did.

Once, only once, he bolted. He pelted into the sky-line, and I thought he'd never stop. When he did, I was sorry he had. He snapped from the bolt into a buck, then smashed headlong into a rabbit warren. The impact almost buried him in the sandy ground. He bogged up to his girths. I had to step off his back to help him flounder out. You would think he would have been beaten after that; but he wasn't. The fire still glowed in his eyes.

Another time, I was on the wrong side of the river when it came down in flood. At the narrowest ford, it swirled for a hundred yards of muddy foam. Yet Midnight swam it with more confidence than a duck-billed platypus. And when we reached home, after a forty-mile ride, he tried to throw me through the main gates. No distance or work ever seemed to tire him. No kindnesses or special attention ever changed him.

I loved that horse. Loved him for his unbreakableness. I couldn't help it. And I knew that, sooner or later, he'd cripple or maybe kill himself. Probably me, too. I told Ken about it. Told him how I felt that Midnight would never give in. He'd kill himself first. Ken fully agreed. Said I could do what I liked with the horse— shoot him if I wanted to or turn him out.

One morning, while the sun struggled to rise, I led Midnight to a distant part of the station. It was a big area, where brumbies roam. I slipped the halter over his ears and let him go. No pat. No rub. Nothing. He wasn't that kind of horse.

For a long minute his deep red eyes stared at me. Then he trotted away, into the great distances, where he belonged.

Epitaph to Jones'y

Jones'y was a strange man. When I first saw him, he was coming over the skyline, merged in the shadows of a mirage. His long legs seemed to be three times longer than his body in the false reflection of water.

The day had been hot, and the sun was westering. All around me, on the vast plain over which I was riding, whirlie-whirlies swirled and capered. Some were towering into great columns of dust; others were scurrying along the ground in tiny whirlwinds.

At the time I noticed Jones'y, he must have been several miles away. I wasn't greatly interested. I reckoned he was just another swagman, or "sundowner," "waltzing Matilda." There are plenty of them in the back country. They are as much part of the country as the tumbleweeds, or roly-polys, bowling along before the wind; so much so that the cattle and sheep properties make special provision for them in their stores. If a swagman calls, he's given a handout of tea, flour, salt, and meat. Sometimes the meat is fresh; sometimes it's salted. But whatever it is, the swagman is given enough tucker to carry him on for a few days until he reaches the next station. If there's a job going, he can have it—always providing that he wants it—and that anchors him for a month or so, but seldom for much longer. Once a man has had dust in his boots, he usually can't stay anywhere for long.

As Jones'y was several miles away, I took no more notice of him. I knew we were heading for the same waterhole. It was directly between us, and the only one for some thirty-odd miles. There were a few stunted trees clustered around it, sufficient to supply enough wood for a man to make a fire and boil the billy.

I reached the waterhole first and unsaddled my mare. I had trained her to stay close to anywhere I camped, so I just slipped off her bridle and turned her loose. While she was having a drink and a roll in the dust to clean the saddle sweat from her back, I lit a fire.

Being busy with my saddlebags and unrolling my blankets, I forgot about Jones'y until I looked up to see him about fifty yards away. He was walking slowly, head held upright, his dusty-booted feet rising and falling in a rhythmic motion.

I squatted back on my heels, expecting him to come and say good day as most travelers do, but he stopped on the other side of the waterhole. He was a tall man, well over six feet, and immensely built, although his body was thin to the point of emaciation. His gaunt face was shadowed under a battered felt hat.

Without looking at me, he carefully set a blackened billy on the ground and unhitched the swag from his shoulders. He set that on the ground, too. Then he began searching around for sticks to make a fire.

I was puzzled. For two men to camp twenty yards apart at an isolated waterhole without sharing the same campfire or speaking to each other seemed too unreal to be true. I stood up and walked over to have a yarn with him. I thought I'd tell him not to bother to make a fire; he could use mine, which was burning brightly.

When Jones'y looked up from his stick gathering, I nodded the usual good day. For a long minute he held his bent body motionless. Then he nodded and went on gathering sticks.

When he had a large armful, I watched him build a crow's nest with them and tuck a handful of dried leaves in the middle. Then he struck a match to light the leaves.

All the time he was doing this, neither of us said a word. There was something extraordinary about Jones'y. I couldn't tell what it was, but I felt as if I couldn't or didn't want to speak in his presence.

Finally, as he was about to stand his billy in the flames, I suggested he come over with me and have some tucker. I had plenty of tinned stuff. Jones'y's own tucker bags looked almost empty.

He acted as if he hadn't heard me. Slowly—all his movements were slow and methodical—he pushed the billy into the fire until flames licked around it. Then he stood to his full height.

He was impressive. He must have been a magnificent man at some time or other, but he was thin. His wide, flat shoulders came into the thinnest waist you ever saw on a grown man. The belt around the top of his frayed trousers was strained in tight, to keep them up.

Jones'y's hat was pulled low over his face, but it couldn't hide his eyes. In a land where men's eyes are habitually bloodshot from sun and dust, Jones'y's were as brilliant as ice and focused on something far beyond me. They stared over my shoulder as if searching the bloody streaks of sunset for a color that wasn't there.

He thanked me, but said he would rather eat on his own. He preferred it that way. His low, husky voice was like his frame—magnificent. It vibrated against the warm stillness left by the dying sun.

I didn't argue. You couldn't argue with a man like Jones'y. You felt as if he wasn't really there; as if he'd gone beyond you, out somewhere to where his eyes were searching. I said good night and went back to my own fire. After a wash and tidy up, I had a meal.

Later, when I rolled over in my blankets to settle down for the night, I looked across at Jones'y. He was still sitting by the embers of his fire. I couldn't tell whether he was dozing or staring out into the darkness.

When I awoke in the morning, it was still dark. Jones'y was gone. After the sun had climbed up out of the dust, I searched the skyline for him. He was already a mile or two away and difficult to see in the early morning haze. I wondered where he was heading, who he was, and why he was as he was. There seemed to be something immeasurably sad or lonely about him.

I'd camped before with swagmen—many of them strange men—but none quite like Jones'y. Even though he was gone, the atmosphere around the little waterhole was still dominated by him. I was glad to saddle my mare and ride on.

For a day or two, I thought a lot about Jones'y, but as I was heading into country I'd never been in before, I soon had other things to occupy my mind.

I was offered a job in a cattle mustering camp and took it. Most of the men in the camp were old-timers—men who'd been in the district a long time.

One night, when we were all sitting around the fire yarning about things in general, the talk swung around to some of the strange characters who people the outback, and I remembered the night I'd camped at the little waterhole. I started to describe Jones'y; but I had no need to. They all knew him.

"That'd be Jones'y," they said.

That was how I came to know his name. One or two of them went on to talk about him. One old-timer reckoned back and said it must be all of fifteen years since he'd first seen Jones'y. Jones'y was a nickname that'd been given him. No one knew his right name. He'd never told anyone what it was.

From the men's talk, it seemed that he just walked, on an endless circuit, covering hundreds, perhaps thousands, of miles. He showed up regularly on the same track every six months; never varied.

Earlier, he'd been offered work. But Jones'y's far-distanced eyes, staring over the offerer's shoulder, had seen things that the offerer could not see. And Jones'y's deep, drawling voice had always said that he had to be somewhere by sundown.

So gradually, he came to be accepted for what he was, or what people thought he was. No one questioned him. The strange, deep, melancholy aloofness that had affected me affected others. They left him alone.

Station storekeepers or managers, who saw his tall, gaunt figure striding out of the horizon, set out rations for him. If he wanted them, he took them. If not, he left them alone. His needs were few. It's doubtful whether he ever ate properly.

I sat for a long time listening to the men talk and wondering what made a fine-looking man like Jones'y lead such an existence. What drove him on? He wasn't mad. Everyone was agreed on that. There were no signs of insanity about him, in any shape or form—just some great restlessness.

The next time I saw Jones'y, I was farther north, but still more or less in the same district. I had driven out to service a windmill bore that was in need of some attention. On the way back, I branched off onto a dusty track that wound through barren mulga country. Why I did it, I don't know. The road I had been following was a shorter route home; but you know how it is. You get a sudden hunch for no apparent reason, and over goes the wheel.

Anyway, when the track straightened out for a mile

or so of straight going, I saw a swagman ahead of
me. Something about the tall, wide-shouldered figure
seemed familiar. Although I'd only seen him once
before, I knew at once who it was. It was Jones'y.

When I drew abreast of him, I stopped the utility
truck and climbed out, hoping I might be able to give
him a lift. Standing in the dust of the roadside, he
looked more gaunt than I had remembered. His great
body was little more than a barely covered framework
of bones.

He slowly stroked one hand down the side of his
sun-blackened face. The other hung loosely, fingers
hooked in the wire handle of the black billy. I offered
him a lift. He shook his head. There was an awful tired-
ness about him. Yet he held his body straight. In their
deep-sunk sockets, his clear blue eyes stared out over
my shoulder, as if he regretted the time being wasted.
He wanted to be on his way.

Then he asked me if I was carrying any water in
the truck. Could I fill his billy? Said he hadn't had a
drink for over twenty-four hours.

I filled his billy and offered him some tucker from
the box I had in the truck. He shook his head. Just
thanked me for the water. That was all. I tried again
to get him to accept a lift. It was no use. He was
already walking, holding the billy out from his side. He
hadn't had a drink from it. I suppose he was going to
wait and boil the water for tea.

I could've cried at the loneliness of him as he walked
away. He made you feel like that; made you feel as if

you would like some good woman to look after him. Yet maybe it was a woman who had made him as he was. I drove past him.

The last remembrance I have of Jones'y is the one I saw in my rear-vision mirror. His tall figure was merging into a receding skyline of sun and dust. Maybe it was the dust that made my eyes raw.

The next time I heard of him, he was dead. Two opal prospectors found his body half buried in drifting sand. He'd been dead for some time. He'd finally wandered away from the tracks he'd followed for so long, into a maze of treacherous sandhills. Perhaps he'd seen there what he wanted to find. He could not have been lost. Jones'y knew a thousand miles of dusty tracks and byways.

The two prospectors hobbled their camels and buried Jones'y. They buried him deep, away from the dingoes and crows. And because, like everyone who knew Jones'y, they thought a lot of him, they made a good job of his grave.

One of them stripped away the bark of a desert needlewood tree and wrote on it with a piece of red-hot fencing wire:

"Old Jones'y's here, all six feet two,
We buried him, as bush blokes do.
We tied his feet and strapped his chin,
His journey's done, just let him in."

Bush Camels

The pub drowsed. Other than me, not a customer leaned on the bar. And it was hot—roasting hot. You could feel the sun crawling over the rooftop.

Across the bar, Joe wiped his face. He used the towel kept mostly for wet glasses.

"Phew!" he said. "She's hotter than fire. You wonder a man lives here."

It's a question often asked. The fierce inland sun sears your marrow; the flies send you groping mad. I nodded, to let him know I wondered, too, then pushed upright.

"So long," I told him. "It's time I was on my way. I'll make Ole's Creek by sunset."

Ole's Creek is a camp, with good dry feed and water. Outside the pub, my horses dozed, tethered to a rail. With several hundred miles behind them, they needed the best I could find.

I paid for my drinks, then tightened my belt as hoofbeats thudded outside. The man who came in through the doorway wore the biggest hat I've seen. The rest of his garb was gray. Gray shirt; gray moleskins; and a gray, sweaty neckerchief folded around his neck.

"Good day," he said to me, then slid a bank note to Joe. "The name's Dean. Charlie Dean, of Nandoola. Set 'em up, Joe, with caps on. A man's swallowed dust since daylight." To ease his legs, he hooked a boot on the rail.

Joe came to life. "Sure," he said. "This joker was just leaving. I'd have been left alone with the flies." He frothed beer as Charlie turned to me.

"Stay with it," he suggested, "for another round or two. She's hot out there on the track."

So I came to meet Charlie—Charlie Dean of Nandoola.

Sprawled elbow-rested, we yarned about things in the West. Cattle; horses; the way of life we knew. And the men we knew. Drovers; horsebreakers; prospectors; motley wanderers who people the great outback.

Suddenly, Charlie thumped the bar. "Say," he said. "Weren't you in Whitecliffs? The bloke who rode the camel?"

On learning I was, Charlie shouted for another round.

"Keep 'em comin', Joe," he said. "We're old mates. We may take a crack at some camels." Then he went on in a roundabout fashion to outline his idea.

On Nandoola, he ran a few head of cattle—maybe five hundred; maybe a thousand. He wasn't sure. But in the dry time prevailing, he hadn't enough to make a living. Among other problems, brumbies and wild camels, as well as donkeys, trampled and grazed his land. The camels ate scrub, which was good cattle feed; the brumbies ate grass, which was already scarce. To help out, Charlie shot the brumbies for their manes and tails—horsehair brought a good price in Sydney.

But the camels had him worried, really worried. They knocked down the few short runs of fence he'd erected and fouled the drying water supplies for his cattle. The big, soft-padded beasts were difficult to track and difficult to shoot. They spent their days in dry, inaccessible country; their nights, padding silently in to drink at a watering point or graze on edible scrub.

Nandoola spread over a hundred odd thousand acres. This gave the camels a fair amount of room to move around in—and space in which to outwit Charlie. Wild camels have more cunning than either brumbies or donkeys. Also, to give them an added advantage, Nandoola was bounded by two very big cattle-stations, both of them, for the most part, unfenced. Wild stock or domestic could come and go at will.

At this stage, I rocked to the door. The sun was westering, and I had a thought for my horses. But Charlie called me back.

"A few more minutes," he said, "then come on home with me. My shack's twenty miles west from here."

Elbows hooked again, we shouldered close, while Charlie ended his story.

"The gist of it is," he went on, "I've had an offer.
An Afghan offered a tenner for every camel I can yard.
He says he'll take up t' thirty."

The offer sounded a good one. Yet I still hadn't
learned where I figured.

"All right," I said. "He'll buy your camels. What's
worryin' me is my horses. They're pawing holes outside.
If a man doesn't shift 'em, the pub'll fall down."

Charlie saw the way I reasoned.

"Yeah," he said. "We don't want it down on our
heads. Besides, it's gettin' too full. A man can't move
t' breathe."

The three drovers who had come in after Charlie
turned as one man. The biggest hitched his pants. I
heard Joe suck his breath.

"So," the big drover grunted, "she's gettin' too full.
If that's how she is, it's outside, mate, on yer neck."

He swung a fist that ripped over Charlie and
thumped me on the ear. I went down pole-axed, trying
to dodge Charlie as I fell. But my luck was out. He
trampled over the top of me, to get at the drover. One
boot gouged my chest; the other tore a strip off my
arm. I had to struggle before I could stagger up.

With me on my feet, the fight became general. One
of the drovers hopped from side to side to make the
battle even.

At one time he'd yell, "I'm with yer, boys," then
slug shoulder to shoulder with Charlie and me.

The next, he'd skip across to the opposite side and

113

shout, "She's on, mates. I'm back into line. Give the bar flies steam."

But like all good things, the fight had to end. Charlie slammed the big drover into a corner, and I cracked another after him. That left us two to one, though the other two were scrambling up.

Charlie called off the fight.

"She's off," he said. "We had a good 'go,' an' we'll say it's quits. Me an' Reg here have got to get crackin'."

After consultation, the drovers agreed.

"Yeah," the big one said. "You could say it was fair. Maybe we'll meet up again. The next time'd be for real."

The other two nodded. "Yeah," one agreed, "you could say we might. The two of 'em ain't so bad."

Satisfied all around, we wiped the blood from our faces. Joe filled the glasses for a final shout; then Charlie and I made our way to the door, thumped on the back by six hard hands.

"We'll see yer next time," the big drover shouted as we climbed up into our saddles, "an' we'll have a longer spell. Git down to some real, solid bashing."

Charlie waved his hand while we jogged around the corner.

"Yeah," he called. "Me an' Reg'll do ya' proper."

The drovers chuckled when they heard him and shoulder-bumped together through the doorway again. We heard them singing to Joe long after we had left— sound carries far on the quiet bush tracks.

On the ride to his shack, Charlie finally reached a conclusion.

"Look at it this way, Reg," he said. "On my own, I can't do the job. It'll take two to run them brumbie camels. An' two to handle 'em once they're caught, though the Afghan only wants 'em taught t' lead. It's tucker for you an' a spell for your horses—plus two quid a head bonus."

Leg-spread in the saddle, I thought it over. The pros and cons were for, rather than against. In the dry country, your horses come first and foremost. A spell, or rest, can do wonders for them, even under the driest conditions—and it really was dry at the time.

"All right," I said. "You can count me in."

We shook hands, leaning across our pommels.

Charlie's shack was rough. There's no other word for it. Big timber slats nailed upright for walls, and a corrugated iron roof. The door swung on greenhide hinges. Water came from a tall, creaking windmill, pumping up from a deep, hand-sunk well.

"She's good," Charlie said as we slid from our saddles. "Every last drop of 'er. Clear as crystal, and no alkali. Just like rain water." It was, too, when we helped each other to a dipperful.

That night was a night to remember. After unsaddling our nags, we turned them loose in a horse paddock.

"They'll be right," Charlie said. "There's a fence all around."

Padding quietly through the dust, we scuffed across

to the shack. Outside, Charlie lit a lantern before pushing open the door. Odd things in my life have surprised me—inside the shack was one of them. Two dogs and a "joey" kangaroo sat facing our entrance. The dogs peered, watchful-eyed; the young kangaroo pawed his whiskers.

Charlie tipped his enormous hat, and a grin twisted the scar that had been hidden.

"So help me." He chuckled. "You'd think I'd been lost. You c'n go out for the evenin'."

Kangaroo in the lead, the three filed into the night.

"A man . . ." I started to say, but Charlie cut me short.

"Don't worry," he said. "They're as good as they come."

Bent over, he raked the coals in the fireplace. Within minutes, he had a billy on to boil.

We were halfway through our meal when the animals filed in again. Charlie had their tucker on the table—corned beef for the dogs; damper for the joey.

"It's right." He nodded. "An' don't crowd. There's plenty for all."

Joey first, the animals obeyed, and they did as Charlie said—neither bolted nor pushed up quickly to grab the food.

From my seat on a box, I had to say something.

"They're good," I said, "an' the joey's as fat as mud."

Charlie was pleased. He pushed his hat farther back until it almost slipped from his head.

"Yeah," he said. "I've had 'im since a nipper. Shows what damper an' a bit of stew can do."

Then he went on to tell me how he'd reared the baby kangaroo—first on tinned milk, then gradually on a mixed diet of, more or less, the food he ate himself. Our meal was ended when he finished.

With the plates stacked, he unhooked a concertina.

"We'll finish the day," he said, "with some music. There's a bottle under the bunk, if you'll fish it out."

While I groped, he tuned into key.

"Don't want t' tune 'er high," he added, "or we'll never reach. You'd need t' be good in the tonsils."

From there on, we shook the old shack. Men lead strange lives in the great, lonely bush. Halfway down the bottle, I did a dance I'd learned from the aborigines.

"Lovely," Charlie chanted. "Keep 'er goin', mate. I'll come in with the bass when we git t' the didgeri-doo."

He did, too, and nearly burst the concertina. Yet his hat still stayed on his head. Mine had long since been tossed in a corner; I'd noticed the joey take a sniff or two at the brim, but the dogs sat quiet and thoughtful, watching my intricate steps.

Morning found us up before sunrise. Raw-eyed, from two hours' sleep, we brewed strong, black tea. Charlie fed his animals, but we were content with tea.

"A man ain't right," Charlie grunted, while we sipped from our mugs, "until he's put in a day. Back comes ya' appetite for a decent bit of tucker." I had to admit I felt much the same.

As a first day, we decided to reconnoiter; take a ride over some of the country where Charlie knew the camels to be.

"We'll cover about forty miles," he said, "an' try t' pick fresh tracks. While we're out, I'll show you where I reckon to trap. It's an old soak bed, now a dry, sandy gully. One end, an' the sides, are blocked completely."

While we talked, the sun began to show. You could feel the promise of another red-hot day.

Later, mounted on two of Charlie's horses, we rode away from the shack. Behind us trotted the two dogs. The joey kangaroo stayed propped on his tail near the windmill. From along the track, I glanced back to see how he was faring. He was still tail-propped, staring after us.

Nandoola is rugged country, eroded and seared by sun. We rode for several miles before we came to see the worst of it. Great towers of carved sandstone withered and broken beyond description; then on into scrub country, where every shrub looked the same. Mile after mile stretching away to sandy, desert regions.

Passing a clump of mulga, Charlie voiced the thoughts of all bushmen.

"She'd be a great country if we only had rain. Just enough of it to hold the ground together."

He tipped back his hat. I saw the scar glow red in the sun. For the first time, I understood why he wore such a wide-brimmed hat.

Most of the day we searched the scrub and desert

country. Because of their pads, camels mostly stay away from rocky ground, or even hard, bare earth. In sand, it's difficult to tell whether tracks are fresh or old, but the droppings give you a clue. It's the same on grassy flats, where a camel leaves little mark; you need the eye of an aboriginal to see where the grass has bent.

Sprawled in the hollow between two sand dunes, we found the bones of a camel that hadn't long been dead. Crows had picked the skeleton to a yellowy whiteness; dingoes, too, had helped in the cleaning.

"The bulls do that," Charlie said. "They'll fight t' the death when they're in season." Then he added, as an afterthought, "You know, it's the bulls that come into season. Not the cows, like in other breeding beasts."

Not being a camel man, I didn't know. But I had seen the bulls in camel teams, worked up to a frothing, moaning state.

"No," I told Charlie, "but you live an' learn, though the learning's not much use. A man's not likely to breed camels for a living."

Charlie saw the point before I'd finished.

"You're right," he said. "Dead, flamin' right. They may've had their place. But the only good 'un now is a dead one. Excepting, of course, if we yard a few for the Afghan. At a tenner apiece, they're useful."

Having seen good, edible scrub fouled and stripped bare by the animals, Charlie's feelings were easy to understand. A stockman in the outback country values every mouthful of feed and treasures it for his cattle.

This may sound strange on such vast holdings, but is an accepted fact. A blade of grass is valued beyond rubies.

"Sure," I said, "I know how you feel. Yet, apart from the bones, we haven't seen a camel—not even the switch of a tail."

Charlie's answer was to point with his whip. On a far-crested sand ridge, a cluster of camels stood, head to rump. Their color, against the sand, made them indistinct; blurred, almost, to the hump and ridge of dunes.

"You see?" Charlie said. "Now watch 'em carve it into the blue."

Hands crossed on pommels, we eased in our saddles. On the far-off ridge, the camels stirred with one motion, then faded from our sight. One second you could see the blur of their movement, then nothing. Just a wisp of dust, trailing, after their passing. Within moments they were blended into raw, red landscape.

At the end of our long ride home, Charlie and I mustered twenty-odd bullocks into cattle yards near the shack. As the gates slammed, joey came to meet us. From there on, we had three followers home.

After unsaddling, Charlie boiled the billy.

"We'll have a bite," he said, "then knock over a bullock. There's some hard yacker ahead of us, an' we'll need good tucker. Plenty of meat to cling to our ribs."

It was dark when we crawled through the cattle-yard rails. Charlie carried a thirty-two rifle; I carried knives and a chopper. Under the big gallows, similar to those on every station, Charlie took his stand.

"Drive 'em toward me," he whispered, "then duck for yer life. I'll take a shot at the first one, soon as I see his eyes." It's tricky work in the dark, but practice is a big factor.

Charlie stood upright behind a gallows post. I crept behind the bullocks. When I made a sudden movement, they bolted straight at Charlie. He waited till they were almost on top of him, then squeezed the trigger. A big bullock tumbled, shot squarely between the eyes. The others broke away, and I threw open the gates. The bullocks bumped their way past me, out into the night. I heard them jostle and bawl, galloping around the windmill.

Bent over, Charlie and I part stripped the carcass on the ground before hoisting it on the gallows. From there on, the work was easy. Charlie disemboweled, while I dressed away the skin, then split the brisket down. The carcass hung neat and workmanlike.

"That's fine," Charlie said, from somewhere near my ear. "Quick an' smart on the trimmin'. You ain't too bad on the knife, but you swung a bit on the choppin'. I had the thought you'd be hoppin' on one leg."

Tired and bloody, we stripped off near the windmill. Charlie dowsed me with bucket after bucket of water, and, in turn, I dowsed him. Dripping water, we padded through the hot, dark night to the shack for a final billy of tea. Naked at the table, with the dogs and joey looking on, we discussed the carcass.

"Let it set for about four hours," Charlie said, "an' we'll take it down before daylight. What we can't keep fresh, we'll cut into pieces an' salt."

Yawning, he stretched out on the one and only bunk mattress. I unrolled my blankets on the floor. Soon we were both asleep.

True to his words, Charlie roused me before daylight. Our clothes were still hanging on the windmill, and we had to pad down there, barefooted, to get dressed. They were stiff with sweat, but we soon bent them into shape.

By lantern light, we cut and salted the meat. Two big steaks were sizzling in the pan as the sun showed raw on the skyline. I've never tasted meat with a fuller, richer flavor.

"It's the saltbush"—Charlie nodded—"an' a touch of gidgea scrub. She's the finest cattle country a man could find in the world."

Big words, maybe; but Charlie was a big man—he had to be, to survive on Nandoola.

With the steak eaten, we shouldered our saddles and bridles to the cattle yards. The two dogs were there, waiting with the horses—they had brought them in while Charlie and I had our meal.

"That's the beauty of 'em," Charlie told me. "They c'n nip out twice as quick as I can to round up the nags. An' it saves a man walking. The thing t' see is when joey goes along for company. The nags get choked at the thought of a 'roo following 'em."

The bush is full of strange sights, but a kangaroo

helping to muster horses must be one of the strangest.

"Yeah," I said. "It would be, at that. I'll look forward to seeing 'im."

Having had our reconnoiter, Charlie decided on action.

"First up," he said, as we jogged along, "we'll tidy the gully. See for sure that there's no outlets. Then cut a stack of scrub to block the free end."

We both had axes strapped to our saddles. They hung with leather guards buckled over the blades.

For our purpose, the gully was ideal—a long, sandy bottom ending in a sharp vee. The sides and one end were sheer, high sandstone rock. Even a goanna couldn't have crawled out up them. At one time, in the distant ages when Australia was young, water had flowed over the sand. The apex, or point of the vee, had probably been a spring. Now it was as dry as any part of the harsh, barren country.

"If she only flowed," Charlie wished when we had slid from our horses and tethered them, "I'd be a wealthy man. I could treble the cattle I carry an' go on t' bigger things. Irrigation an' the lot." Under the big hat, his face looked wistful.

All morning we cut and carried. A great mound of brush spread all along the gully's end. We left a gap and a pile of scrub, ready cut, to fill it after the camels entered—that's if they ever entered.

"It's a chance," Charlie agreed, while we sprawled for our noon-day spell, "an' a chance that's worth the takin'. You never know how it is with luck."

123

Under the rock where I'd crawled for shade, a lizard sat up to watch me. Charlie lay under a tent of fresh-cut scrub.

"No," I said. "But there's a lot of ridin' between us an' the camels. The thing is, where do we start? As far as I've seen, it's sand, scrub, an' rock, an' the sight of a few camel humps."

I heard Charlie sigh as he rolled over. The sand felt hot underneath, even in the shade. You could feel the heat burn through.

"Don't worry," he said. "We'll find 'em. Then it's up to us t' yard 'em in the gully."

His voice turned to a snore, and we slept for an hour in the dust. I awoke to find the lizard nibbling at my boots.

All afternoon we combed the scrublands, then veered across to the sandhills. Up sliding ridges and down into hollows, our horses slithered and labored. We saw tracks—but no camels. The great, smelly beasts had padded and churned; yet not one showed. We saw hair where they had rolled; droppings where they had traveled; even caught the smell of their rank, sour saliva.

As Charlie said, "You c'n smell 'em for miles. But you can't see their humps or the snarl of their nostrils."

It was dark when we jogged our way to the shack. Two tired men, we had barely eaten before we stretched full length on our blankets.

The next day, Charlie accidentally discovered, was a Sunday. He found out by thumbing through a calendar.

We were eating breakfast by lantern light, and he thought he would check the date.

"So help me," he said, "we ought t' be in bed. I allus have another half hour t' show me respects."

Stumping to the door, he whistled shrilly for the dogs to return—he'd sent them ten minutes before to bring the horses. Back at the table again, he fed joey a piece of damper.

"That was close," he went on. "The nags were half-way in. I could hear 'em pounding. Now the thing is, what about it? What d' you say to a swim in me best waterhole an' a bit of 'scran' on the banks? We could go in the car that I keep out back."

I had seen the car parked under a tree. It was an old vintage model, and very decrepit.

"Sure," I said. "It'd go down fine. An' be a change from camels—the camels we haven't seen. But does the car go? She seems t' me all wire an' string."

Charlie laughed until I thought he would strangle. When he could breathe, he thumped the table.

"Strewth!" he choked. "She'll start all right. Another ruddy feather, an' she'd fly. You couldn't fault 'er over my sort of goin'."

I found out later he was right. When we climbed aboard, the dogs, crouched with joey, had the tucker-box between them on the back seat. Charlie and I sat leg-braced in the front. The open sides let in wind and weather, and the sun blazed on our heads. The canvas hood had long since withered away, though the stays remained. Charlie used them to hang the billy on, and odd coils of wire or tools. He was a practical man; everything had its use.

The start was perfect. Two warning coughs, then a sudden, tremendous buck. Dogs, kangaroo, tucker-box, Charlie, and me, all heaved upward in a back-breaking motion, then sank backward. The car was off, with a grinding gear crash.

"You can't ease 'em in," Charlie shouted. "She won't have it if you do. You've got to slam 'em, or they'll stick in neutral."

To prove his point, he slammed in another one. We raced at well over thirty.

Passing the windmill and leaving the cattle yards behind, we each cocked a leg over the windshield—or I should say, where the windshield had been. Along with the hood, it had gone with time and weather. Hats tipped forward, we stared at the hot, dry landscape or drowsed for a second or two of sleep.

From one of these sessions, Charlie roused long enough to say, "She's like an old horse. You can't shake 'er feet from the track. All you want is your hand on the bridle, an' she'll do the rest."

Exaggeration or not, I was too at ease to worry. The sun poured hot on my head, and the car made a welcome change from my saddle. As far as I could see, he seemed to be right. More often than not, his hand just rested on the wheel, one foot on the accelerator.

Toward noon the track wound up a crest before lipping over into a hollow. Charlie stirred to straighten his back on the seat. The cocked-up leg slid down to join the other.

"Here she is," he told me. "Just over the rise. The best flamin' lagoon on Nandoola."

He had barely finished when the car spluttered up and over; all pistons racing, she bowled down toward the water. But Charlie stopped her dead, skewering her around on the track.

Ahead of us, dozing near the waterhole, stood at least a hundred camels. They were as startled as we were. Cows, calves, and several big old bulls stared slack-lipped and drooling. But not for long. As one, they surged in a leggy, jostling mob and were gone; a hundred jolting humps disappeared up a gully. All that remained was the rankness of their droppings.

"Well I'll be hamstrung," was the best I could say.

But Charlie surpassed me. The air turned blue for several minutes.

When he had cooled, he tipped back his hat before restarting the car.

"What did I tell you?" he asked me. "Just what did I say? They'd break a cattleman's heart."

Still rubbing my leg where I'd cracked it on the dashboard, I had to admit they would. Yet, in a way, I felt sorry for the big brutes. At one time useful, now no longer wanted, except by an odd Afghan teamster, or maybe wandering aboriginal, they have bred and multiplied like the wild horses and donkeys. They have to be destroyed; yet there's a sadness in their passing—

though they'll never be completely obliterated; the wild, rugged bushlands will see to that.

On the short run down to the lagoon, I kept these thoughts to myself. It's easy to moralize when you don't own cattle or a property. Under a spindly tree, Charlie parked his panting car. The dogs hopped out one side, joey the other.

Charlie and I sat quietly for a few moments, to stare at the long lagoon. The sight of water does that to a man in hot, dry country. You almost forget what a sheet of water can look like. Finally, we unhooked our legs to climb out. Charlie voiced the thoughts of both of us.

"It'd be great," he said, "if you had holes the same all over. There'd be water t' spare for every flamin' beast."

It would, too. Lack of water is the curse of inland Australia.

We stripped for a swim. Tender-toed over the stony places, we hobbled our way to the water. Charlie kept his hat on to shield the sun from his face. I was as free as nature made me, though a bit more skewbald in color—brown from the waist up; white from the waist down. Charlie slapped in first, holding his hat tightly to his head.

"Lovely," he spluttered as I plunged in alongside. "You c'n feel it soak in. A man gets cracks in his hide."

Cracks or not, the water felt beautiful. As Charlie said, you could feel it soak in. He was not worried about fouling. The lagoon had the depth and width of an outback river, with overflow outlets at each end, and was not landlocked. Besides, the water was never used for human consumption—Charlie saw to that.

For an hour or more we soaked and swam. Then, more soft-footed than ever, we hobbled again to the car. Boots were the immediate things pulled on. After them, trousers and shirts slipped on more slowly. There's a pleasure in dressing while still wet—you stay cooler longer.

The rest of the day we lazed contentedly; a mug of tea in one hand and, at odd times, a meat-damper sandwich in the other. Joey and the dogs sprawled sleepily near us. Early in his youth, joey had been gelded. He had no urge for the wide, open spaces. His life centered around the dogs and Charlie. In a way, you could say they were one happy family.

With Sunday over, we felt time was pressing. The urge moved in us to tackle the camels. In the dark of Monday morning, Charlie sent his dogs for the horses.

"That mob we saw," Charlie stated, while I kneaded dough, "was a gatherin'. They do that every so often. The same as you'll see cattle or horses. They'll be split now an' runnin' in their own little mobs—maybe ten or twenty to the bunch. But we'll have a good chance t' pick up fresh tracks."

As he finished, I buried my dough in ashes—the best of damper is baked in hot coals. Charlie himself cut the last of our precious steak. From there on, we had only salted beef.

I said, "That's the way they'll be. An' too far out for

a daily trip with horses. We'd best camp out till we snare some—or have a crack at tryin'."

Charlie liked to use his shack as a base, yet he agreed with my reasoning. We left at daylight, with a string of six horses and enough food for several days. The dogs and joey stayed to roam at will around the shack. Enough bullock bones remained for the dogs to gnaw; joey could graze where he wished.

"They're right," Charlie nodded as we jig-jogged away from the cattle yards. "It's home, sweet home to them. Between 'em, they own the place. I'm just a workin' partner."

Toward noon, we reined in under a clump of mulga scrub. The spindly trees cast broken shade, and the boughs were handy to hang our utensils. A burly pack-horse carried water for our drinking and cooking use, while the horses themselves would have to drink at a gilgii a mile or two away. Around the clump was a fair covering of dried, sun-cured grass. All in all, a fair camp.

"She'll do," Charlie said as we unloaded, "an' it ain't too far from the trap."

As near as we could judge, the gully was three miles west—a good distance, if we had luck, to run any camels.

After a billy of tea, we changed to two led horses. Hats tipped against the sun, we ambled on our first excursion. And it was an excursion, without any frills— just plain, slogging riding across bare, barren ridges.

In a line with the lagoon's direction, we came on a

splatter of tracks, but lost them on swept, bare clay-pans. The spongy hoofs neither brushed nor marked. Back-riding again, we found another cluster of fairly fresh prints and lost them, too.

Raw-eyed from glare, we rode until the sun sank bloody-red, then rode to our camp in the dark. We were tired when we hunkered down near a fire, though gulps of hot tea soon revived us.

Morning told a different story. Charlie boiled the billy, while I walked, stiff-legged, to bridle two of our hobbled horses. It was still dark when I vaulted onto one and led the other in toward camp. Ahead of me, I could see the small, bright twinkle of fire as it showed through Charlie's legs.

Suddenly, I heard grunts away to the right and the crackle of scrub being pulled. Somewhere in the dark, camels were feeding; I even thought I could smell their rank, tangy odor.

Riding carefully so as not to scrape any mulga limbs, I nudged the horses into camp. Close to the fire, I whispered down to Charlie that camels were feeding near; no more, maybe, than a quarter of a mile. Charlie's immediate move was to vault up beside me.

"No time for saddles," he grunted, "or breakfast either. Lead on, Reg, an' I'll be behind you."

Single file, we padded away from the camp. Charlie's horse nosed close to the tail of my own.

Guided by an occasional grunt or coughing snarl, we rode in a wide semicircle to take positions on the far side of the camels. Given daylight, we would close in and hope for the best; drive them toward the gully, where the brush fence waited.

In the way of wild, scary animals, the camels began to drift before light. We heard them coming nearer to us, while we sweated in the palms and kept our horses moving; kept them angling quietly in the direction we judged the camels were going. Then the first raw streaks of color appeared up on the skyline to outline scrub and camels.

As one man, Charlie and I leaned over our horses' withers in a wild, headlong gallop. The camels had already bolted, warned by their outlaw instinct. We heard them snarl as they crashed through scrub and bush.

Close to a straining horse, without saddle or blanket, you feel his muscles bunch; feel the great beat of his legs and haunches. But gradually, as you get used to the feel, you become part of the horse. It's your legs that are pounding; your muscles knotted with straining. So it was with Charlie and me, hurtling after those racing camels.

At one time I glanced at Charlie. He seemed part of his galloping horse. The two of us yelled, mad as any screaming dervish—or wild bush hatter, if the name suits better. But we wheeled the camels; headed them into the way we wanted them to go. From there on, it was a matter of staying close; keeping them bunched, without time to think.

Rocking with their great, raking strides, they were a sight for an Arab's eyes—or anyone else that loves camels. Ewed, shaggy necks and humped, shaggy backs, they racked at amazing speed. Charlie and I had to ride with hands and spurs to stay in anywhere close.

As full light came, I made a count—twenty-seven head. But at least six were calves; half-grown fellows, pounding flank-to-flank with their mothers. The rest were bulls and cows of varying ages.

Through tangled scrub, up slithery slopes, down into eroded gullies, we galloped, slid, and scrambled. Always in my heart is a love for outback horses. As horse-flesh goes, no finer roams the world. Tough, fast, and durable, they'll gallop where others can't walk. Our two gave of their best in that headlong, crazy ride.

I remember thinking on mine, as I gripped to his heaving back, "You beaut. You iron-mouthed, iron-gutted beaut. A man's life is trusted to every sure-footed hoof." And I rubbed his ears where the sweat was running.

As we neared the gully, the camels tried to split. Some broke to my side; some to Charlie's. For heart-breaking seconds, it seemed we would lose them; lose the whole herd. But, somehow or other, we held them; kept them heading to where we wanted.

I know I slapped my hat in a big bull's face, and I heard Charlie rise to his finest heights of expression; my own straining voice would have blistered a bullock wagon. Then they jostled together in a bumping mob to pound through the open gap. We fell from our horses to close it before they could hammer back.

When the job was finished, we sprawled flat on our backs. Charlie covered his face with his wide-brimmed hat; I stared up to the brassy-blue sky. The sun flared down and could burn, for all I cared. Our horses stood near, sucking air into lungs that must have come close to bursting. Sweat ran in rivers from the four of us.

After a time, Charlie tipped back the hat from his mouth.

"Oh, mate," he said, "that was some flamin' ride. Me legs ain't stopped grippin' yet."

My own felt tight and knotted at the backs. I could feel them twitch if I moved.

"Mine, too," I agreed. "I'm about the same. A man was mad t' do it without a saddle."

Charlie sat up long enough to wipe his streaming face.

"Mad or not"—he chuckled—"we yarded a swag of the stinkers, an' near enough to the number."

With that, he fell backward, flat on his back, and we rested another ten minutes.

To keep the camels from breaking out, we decided to camp on our side. While I brought the remainder of our horses and gear across, Charlie guarded the scrub fence. He had the fire lit, ready for the billy, when I returned, and we ate a late noon-day breakfast. The cold salt beef tasted good, washed down with steaming black tea. Mugs in hand, after eating, we worked out the next stage in our proceedings.

"This arvo'," Charlie said, "we'll let 'em settle an' take it easy ourselves. Fill a few sandbags to anchor 'em when we catch 'em. That way, they'll teach to lead an' at the same time won't hurt themselves."

The method he had in mind is a method used by horsebreakers. You strap a ring on a full bag of sand, then tie the colt to the ring. The bag gives a little, where a post won't. The colt can pull and play around as much as he likes, but not hurt his legs or neck. It seemed to me as good a way as any to use on the camels.

"Sure." I nodded. "We'll try it, to see how it goes. There's a lot of sweat yet between us an' the last one."

Charlie could still see the humor of it when, later, we shoveled sand into the bags.

"You know, Reg," he told me. "You're a funny codger. Funny in more ways than one. But you're a ruddy good mate, an' a man couldn't wish for better."

Coming from Charlie, the words sounded true. He made no bones about his feelings.

The following day we readied for action, tested our girths, and strapped breastplate roping harnesses to our saddles. We cleared the gap to ride through, then closed it after us. Side by side, with greenhide ropes in our hands, we jogged up the gully. Underfoot, the sand kicked up into drifting puffs; to the east, the sun just showed on the skyline.

Watching the blood-raw tints, Charlie swung the rope in his hand.

"Wonderful," he said, "where all them colors come from. You can't tell me there ain't something there. Life, I mean, an' the way a man lives."

Watching, too, as the colors streamed and flamed, I found I had no answer. Instead, I coiled my rope into shape and hoped for the best with our camels.

We found them more or less standing at bay, in the end of the gully. They are strange brutes, and you never know how to take them; even camel teamsters get mauled at times. Yet, again, they can be docile, though complaining.

Our bunch, wild and unbroken, spat and snarled in turn as we rode near—our idea being to each rope the same camel, then jockey it to a sandbag, where we could tie it.

First beast out was a bull, with lips curled away from his teeth. You could see them yellow through the saliva.

"Take him," Charlie shouted, and we both tossed our ropes.

From there on the camel did everything except climb up the ropes in a rope trick. If he tried to rip me from the saddle, Charlie's horse hauled him away. In turn, my horse did his share in pulling the camel from Charlie. Dust, sweat, and camel saliva mixed to a fog in the gully. When it cleared, we had the bull anchored by neck strap and lead to a sandbag.

"Number one," Charlie panted. "An' twenty to go. We won't touch the young 'uns. The Afghan'll take 'em as they are. They'll follow their mothers, anyway."

A five-minute breather gave us time to catch our wind, then remount to rope our next one. It was a cow, and one with a calf at foot. Every move the cow made, the calf followed suit. As he was nearly as big as his mother, we had a lively time. The cow would lunge at one of us, and her calf, dazed by it all, would follow. Having no rope as a check, he would smack into one of our horses.

Horses don't like camels at the best of times. Having a young one trying to climb over their backs gives them an even greater dislike. Ours spent most of the morning fighting back the best way they could—bites, kicks, and violent fits of bucking if a camel's head or neck lodged on their rumps.

By noon, we had eight camels safely anchored and more or less broken to the feel of a rope.

"Great," Charlie said as we rode out through the gap. "Just great. With a bit of luck, we'll finish 'em tomorrow. After that, a day t' settle 'em down, an' we c'n take 'em home to the cattle yards."

In the afternoon we struck a snag. A real, lip-snarling outlaw. He was a young bull; big-humped and big-necked. His slobbering mouth seemed to tower over us when we tossed our ropes. For moments he bellowed and squealed, and I felt my horse give ground. The harness on his chest creaked with the strain being put on it.

"Hang on, Charlie," I shouted. "This one's as strong as ten. Keep 'im moving while I tighten a buckle."

Charlie did his best, but it wasn't good enough. The bull snapped at him, then whipped across to me. He drove his jaws down, and I felt them rub on my back. Teeth, spit, and slobber stunk as I ducked. The next second I was flat on the ground. The bull had clamped his jaws on the cantle with a wrench that sent my horse flying.

From a tangle of hoofs in the dust, I heard Charlie curse as he reefed his horse almost onto its haunches. The rope hummed with the strain he held on it, while my horse scrambled clear.

Swift-moving myself, I rolled from under the camel and hit the saddle with two legs flying. In the time it takes to tell, I tightened the buckle needed, then reined to take a strain. Chewing sand, I glanced to Charlie. The camel reared and snarled between us. I had my doubts of ever getting it tied to a sandbag.

But, in the way of things, we did. Hard, solid work can solve most problems. By the afternoon's end, we had fourteen camels anchored. Later in the evening, we freed them to rest for the night. Hunkered over our fire, we discussed the next day's proceedings.

Charlie summed it up before we turned in by saying, "T'morrow's another day. There's seven t' go, an' we ought t' do it. Given luck, the job'll be finished by the day after." Which is what we wanted—the camels would need a drink by then.

Sleep came slowly that night. I suppose, after a day spent wrestling with camels, we felt a bit jittery. Or maybe we were too tired to sleep. Sand, too, makes a hard bed. Harder than the sun-baked earth we were used to sleeping on. It grinds against you every time you turn.

In the morning, we roused out early. While I pulled on my boots, Charlie kicked the fire together.

"This is the one we've been looking for." He yawned. "So we might as well start it right. Have the horses ready before the sun crawls over our heads."

Yawning myself, I groped where the bridles were hanging. With two on my arm, I plodded away into darkness to find our hobbled nags. Charlie stayed to boil the billy and set a damper in the ashes.

As a first chore after breakfast, we recaught our fourteen camels of the day before. For the most part they answered the rope reasonably enough, and we soon had them tethered.

"By tonight"—Charlie nodded—"they'll be eatin' out of our hands."

Looking at the big, slobbery lips, I had my doubts; but there's no accounting for tastes.

"We'll leave it there," I said, "an' not make the thing too matey. The way I see it, they'd eat your flamin' hand."

Charlie had a simple sense of humor. He was still chuckling when we roped our first fresh camel.

During the morning, we became careless. Careless or tired—it's hard to say which. Long, hot days can beat the best of men. A mangy, sore spotted cow reefed savagely on her rope as we tethered her to a sandbag.

Charlie reached to hitch a knot, and the cow mauled him. Her long yellow teeth slobbered over his arm, then ripped a tear around his elbow. He fell across her neck with the pain of the bite, and she bit him again—

139

this time on the hip. A strip of his trousers came away in her teeth. I heard them grind as she chewed.

At times like that, you move fast. I slapped my hat over her eyes to block her vision, while Charlie crawled clear. It also gave him time to finish tying the hitch. When it was secure, he staggered away, holding his arm and bent over at the hip. I thought for the time he was finished for the day, but he came around after a spell in the shade.

Then it was my turn. The last camel but one kicked me. Its great, shaggy hock smashed into my chest with such force that I hurtled across the gully. Luckily, it was the hock that hit me, not the tough, spongy hoof; the kick couldn't reach its full extent. If it had, I doubt whether I would be writing this story. As it was, I rolled and sweated for minutes. My muscles balled as I tried to suck air. All Charlie could do was watch. He had his hands full, tying the camel.

But, finally, we finished. The last of the scruffy brutes strained, tethered to a bag. The gully seemed full of grunting, tied-down camels. The calves stood close to their mothers.

Raw-handed, raw-eyed, and stiff on our tired horses, we jogged to boil the billy.

"You know," Charlie said as we slid from our saddles, "a man works hard in the bush. An' he gets his share of knocks. There ain't no wonder not many will do the work."

I rubbed my horse's back, then turned him loose. My ribs felt knotted from the kick.

All I could say was, "You can say that again. I'm past any flamin' wonder."

The afternoon passed quietly; so did the evening. We wandered from camel to camel, rubbing their necks and heads. When we freed them for the night, they had become, to an extent, docile. They at least didn't snap at our hands or spit their slobber at us.

Over our final billy, Charlie stroked his arm. It had swollen angrily where the skin was broken.

"We'll shepherd 'em tomorrow," he said, "up an' down the gully. I reckon about nine, it'll be safe to let 'em out. By midafternoon we should be at the cattle yards. Then we c'n cut 'em some scrub."

Stretched on my side, I half sat, propped on an elbow. The firelight glowed bright on Charlie's face. I could see the scar and drooped, tired lines.

"Sure," I said. "We're nearly through. You can't say it's been easy; but, then again, it hasn't been bad. In a week or two we'll forget—forget every hair of their humps."

Charlie drained his mug, then tossed it near the fire. I watched him roll in his swag.

"Not me," he said. "You maybe might. There's mobs of 'em yet, out there in the night."

He pulled the blankets up over his head. I heard him groan as he bumped his arm.

Morning came with its usual sun glare. We packed and tethered our spare horses before riding through the gap. Only lightly closing it, we jogged along the gully to where our camels milled. Charlie nursed his swollen arm; I rode hunched over to ease my bruised chest—it had turned black in the night.

"Get a bit of sun," Charlie hoped, "an' we'll loosen up. Yer can't beat heat to take away pain."

If I talked, I coughed, so I didn't answer. In any case, Charlie wasn't listening. The camels' snarls drowned out most sounds.

We drove them around and around and around. The sun flared down on their humped, hairy backs. Finally, true to his words, Charlie cleared the gap at nine.

"Drive 'em through," he shouted, "while I free the nags. We'll let 'em run in the lead."

By the time the camels snorted out through the gap, the horses were already trotting. Reins tied to necks or looped on packsaddles, they headed straight for home. We drove the bunched camels after them. Stiff after their handling, they trotted freely; harum-scarum at first, but gradually settling. When the cattle yards showed, they were traveling quite quietly.

Charlie's dogs, followed by joey, came to meet our cavalcade. In company with us, they helped water the camels, then drive them into the yards. As the gates slammed, I patted Charlie's shoulder.

"There's a few quid there," I said, "that you owe me. An' a nice little check for yourself."

Charlie's answer was to shake my hand.

"You've earned it," he told me. "Every last flamin' cent. An' as for me, I'm still in the red. They've done more damage to the place than the check'll cover, but it'll help."

Shoulder to shoulder, we rode to the shack. Unsaddled and glad to be home, our horses rolled outside, while Charlie and I drank tea. Then to finish the job for the day, we cut scrub to feed the camels, a mound of it, almost as high as the rails.

A week later, with the camels sold and delivered, I said so long to Charlie.

Standing with the dogs and joey behind him, he somehow looked lonely. The big hat shadowed his face.

"So long, Reg," he said. "I'll miss you, mate. Drop in again, if you're passing."

I told him I would and rode away.

Paths seldom cross in the bush, once you've said so long at parting.